D1613215

The Wandering Gorillas

THE
WANDERING
GORILLAS

Alan Goodall

COLLINS
St James's Place, London
1979

William Collins Sons & Co Ltd
London · Glasgow · Sydney · Auckland
Toronto · Johannesburg

First published 1979
© Alan Goodall 1979

ISBN 0 00 216265 2

Set in Monotype Baskerville
Made and printed in Great Britain by
William Collins Sons & Co Ltd, Glasgow

Dedicated to the many primates who made
this book possible, particularly Margaret,
Patrice, Adrien, Peter; to the late
Sir William Collins; and most of all to the
memory of Kelele as he wandered with his
family through the forests of the Kahuzi-Biega
National Park.

Acknowledgements

In order to have completed this research single-handed I would have needed to be an accomplished diplomat, botanist, geographer, cartographer, nutritionist, vet, conservator, statistician and pygmy tracker – as well as a zoologist. To add impossibility to improbability I would also have had to be my own wife! For this project was only made possible by the unselfish help of many people from diverse fields of interest and of many nationalities. Words alone cannot express my gratitude, but it gives me great pleasure to acknowledge here my debt to all of them. In particular I would like to give my sincere thanks for the help and encouragement of:

The Governments and Park Officials of the Republics of Rwanda and Zaire; the Director General and Staff of INCN and IRSAC – Zaire (particularly Citoyen Tanganyka Gahuranye, Dr Ntika Nkumu, Dr J. Verschuren, Drs Peter and Irene Kunkel, Monsieur Adrien Deschryver and Citoyen L. Mushengi); the Science Research Council, the World Wildlife Fund, the Fauna Preservation Society, Liverpool University, The University of Ghent, the late Dr L. S. B. Leakey, Miss Dian Fossey and her staff at the camp on Mt Visoke, the National Geographic Society, Professor A. J. Cain, Professor R. A. Hinde, Citoyens J. Kalamo, Patrice Wazi-Wazi, all members of 'Mission Scientifique Belge des Volcans de l'Afrique Central: 1971–1972' especially Mlle Christine Marius-Weyns; Mrs Irene Leppington, Mr E. Djoleto-Nattey, Mrs L. Turtle, Dr T. Lawrence, Dr R. G. Pearson, Dr G. A Parker, Dr J. Bishop, Dr S. Bradley, Dr R. White, Dr F. and Mme E. Dondeyne, Dr H. J. and Frau H. Schlichte, Goetz Dieter Plage, and finally, most of all to my wife Margaret.

Finally, I owe special thanks to the late Sir William Collins, who encouraged me to write this book, and to his staff – particularly Gillian Gibbins and Adrian House – for their endless help and understanding during its production.

Contents

Illustrations

Maps

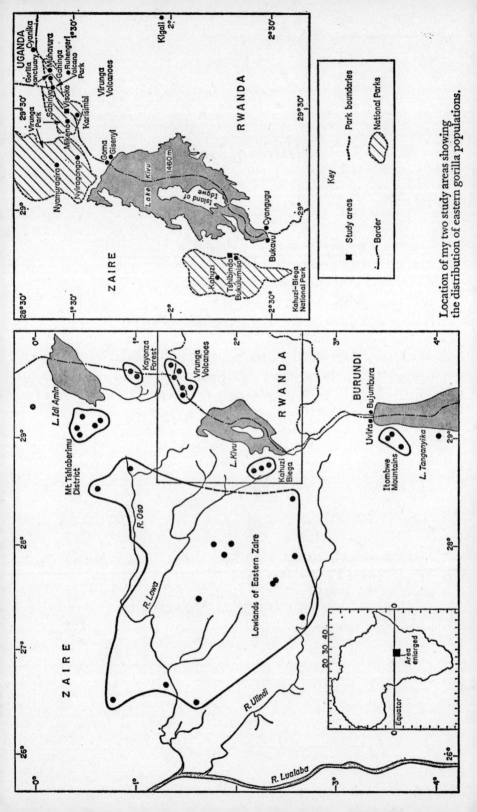

Location of my two study areas showing
the distribution of eastern gorilla populations.

Introduction

It was a fine summer's day in July 1970. Many of my fellow passengers were obviously going on holiday to the Continent and were chatting excitedly about the days ahead. My own thoughts were elsewhere, then suddenly, as the train pulled out of Victoria station, a feeling of panic came over me. Only then did I realize the full implications of the journey on which I was embarking: to study the rare mountain gorilla in its natural habitat.

Three years earlier I had decided to abandon teaching for a time in order to take a degree in zoology at Liverpool University. I soon became enthralled by the excitement of the natural world unfolded by my studies. The more I learned the more fascinated I became by the varied adaptations of organisms to their habitats and by the forces which had shaped these adaptations. In particular I was captivated by a relatively new branch of biological research called Ethology, the study of animal behaviour. During my honours year I became so absorbed by these studies, especially the behaviour of primates, that I decided to try and obtain a research studentship and study for a higher degree.

Monkeys and apes have always fascinated man, probably ever since he first got to know them as competitors during his own early evolution. We are particularly intrigued by the apes because they resemble ourselves more closely than any other living creature. Modern biochemical analysis has shown that the chimpanzee is our closest relative, followed in order by the gorilla, orang-utan, and finally the lesser apes, the gibbons. Chimps, the clowns of the primate world, have been kept in captivity for many years and have been well studied by circus owners, zoo keepers and scientists: they are fairly numerous and widespread in some areas of central Africa, they are relatively easy to capture and to rear and breed in captivity. The other two great apes, however, live more secretive lives in dense, remote rain forests and until recently we knew very little about them in their natural habitats. Doubt and uncertainty, myth and legend, shrouded them in mystery and fear. In the case of gorillas especially this was due to their immense size and strength, for an adult male mountain gorilla can weigh over 400 lbs (200 kilos).

The very existence of gorillas was not known to the civilized world until 1846 when their discovery in West Africa finally settled the rather confused debate as to whether or not the sightings of 'huge black apes' were merely of large chimpanzees. After the scientific description of the lowland gorilla (*Gorilla gorilla*) by Savage and Wyman in 1847, several expeditions went to West Africa to observe, but primarily to 'collect' (shoot) specimens for scientific investigations and museum exhibits.

Amongst the most notable of these expeditions was that of Du Chaillu, who in his book *Explorations and Adventures in Equatorial Africa* (1861) gives the following vivid description of his first contact with a wild gorilla in its jungle home:

> His eyes began to flash fire as we stood motionless on the defensive, and the crest of short hair which stands on his forehead began to twitch rapidly up and down, while his powerful fangs were shown as he again sent forth a thunderous roar. And now truly he reminded me of nothing but some hellish dream creature – a being of that hideous order, half-man half-beast, which we find pictured by old artists in some representations of the infernal regions. He advanced a few steps, then stopped to utter that hideous roar again – advanced again, and finally stopped when at a distance of about six yards from us. And there, just as he began another of his roars, beating his breast in rage, we fired and killed him.

But Du Chaillu's work was apparently written more to gain publicity and fame for his daring as an explorer than to give accurate insight into the natural world, and much of it was later shown to be false.

The existence of another race of gorillas in a separate area of

forest some six hundred miles (1000 km) away among the
remote Virunga volcanoes of central Africa was not discovered
until 1902. An expedition led by Captain Oscar von Beringe,
looking not for gorillas but for opportunities to demonstrate the
power of the German army, climbed Mt Sabinio, one of the
dormant volcanoes in the chain. Whilst climbing, Beringe and
his men spotted some 'large black apes' across a ravine, and
shot two of them. After this initial discovery the 'mountain'
gorilla (*Gorilla gorilla beringei*, as it was subsequently described
by Matschie) was, like its lowland relative, 'studied' by explorers, and some fifty were shot.

Fortunately one collector, Carl Akeley, was so impressed with
the gorillas and their home in the Virunga volcanoes, which he
called 'the most beautiful spot in the world', that he urged the
Belgian King, Albert, to make this area a sanctuary for these
rare apes. Thanks largely to his efforts the Albert National Park
(now Virunga National Park) was created in 1925, and became
the first National Park in the entire continent of Africa. Its
southern portion, together with the recently independent
areas in Rwanda (Volcano National Park) and Uganda (Gorilla
sanctuary), covers all eight volcanoes.

The first useful scientific observations of free-living gorillas
were made by Carl Akeley himself and he began to suspect that
gorillas were not ferocious 'man-killing' apes but were gentle
giants who lived quiet and peaceful lives in their remote and
inhospitable mountain home. Unfortunately the climate proved
to be too severe for Akeley, who tragically died of pneumonia
and was buried by his wife, Mary, at Kabara, Mt Mikeno, the
place of his dreams. The account of their final climb to Kabara
is movingly described by Mary Akeley herself:

> I have said that the Rweru camp was one of the strangest of all
> places. Over it soon fell the shadow of fear for my husband had a
> recurrence of fever and my own anxiety became intense. Alter-
> nately walking and being carried in a hammock he courageously
> continued up the mountainside, and we finally reached our camp
> Kabara on the slopes of Mt. Mikeno . . . It was the beautiful land
> of my husband's dreams – the spot he had longed to reach.
>
> In this wildly beautiful spot, remote almost as another planet,

and with barely time to glimpse this realm of his heart's desire my husband began another journey – the last long pilgrimage.

Akeley's wife and his companion, Derscheid, completed his expedition work and ensured the publication of his valuable findings.

Further scientific expeditions set out to observe and collect mountain gorillas, and found populations in other areas of nearby Rwanda (then Ruanda-Urundi), in the Kayonza forest of Uganda, and in eastern Zaire (Congo). They were more successful with their shooting than in their observations, thus the museums of the world received more and more specimens to mount in their displays but were given conflicting reports about gorilla behaviour. One such expedition, in 1932, ended in disaster when its leader, Harold Bingham, shot an adult male gorilla in the Virunga volcanoes. He claimed that it had charged and was about to attack his wife, and so he was forced to shoot in self-defence. Thus the controversy about the true nature of gorillas raged once more: had Akeley been wrong in saying that gorillas were not ferocious? Were the early explorers like Du Chaillu correct?

Answers to questions like these remained unknown for over twenty-five years. Then, in the mid 1950s Walter Baumgärtel, owner of the Traveller's Rest Hotel, Kisoro, Uganda, realized that the gorillas inhabiting the nearby forests on Mt Muhavura had great potential for tourism and scientific research. He persuaded two world-famous anthropologists, Dr Louis Leakey and Dr Raymond Dart, to promote and raise funds for a pilot research project: this was conducted in 1956–7 by Rosalie Osborn and Jill Donisthorpe. In the following two years independent expeditions were made to the same area by several Japanese scientists. Each of these studies provided extremely useful, though superficial, reports about gorilla behaviour and ecology. In particular their techniques of 'baiting', i.e. placing food in a place to which you wish to entice the animals, were singularly unsuccessful. None of these preliminary projects was extended, indeed the Japanese researchers abandoned their attempts to study free-living gorillas as too difficult, and too dangerous.

Introduction

The final turning point in our understanding of gorilla behaviour came in 1959 when George Schaller and John Emlen started their remarkable study. First they conducted a general survey of gorillas throughout central Africa, followed by a one-year study of the gorilla population at Kabara by George Schaller and his wife. Schaller's subsequent publications provided the answers to many of the earlier controversies. He found that although gorillas did give apparently ferocious charges at human intruders, these were 'bluff' to intimidate the observer. Anyone who faced such charges without running away, and more important without shooting, would not be attacked. He found that gorillas lived in social groups containing anything up to twenty or so members: adult females, with or without infants; juveniles; sub-adults of both sexes; and one (sometimes more) fully adult male, the leader of the group. At maturity the hairs on the back of such males turned silver-grey and hence they were called 'silverbacks'.

Schaller collected a great deal of data about the feeding habits of his study animals, finding them to be exclusively vegetarian. His observations of their social habits showed that they lived in stable mixed groups. Whilst neighbouring groups sometimes met, even mingled and slept near each other at night, they soon separated and kept their autonomy. In the field of primate research this study set new standards for methods of observation and data recording. Most of all, it demonstrated that even gorillas could be studied in their natural habitat by the process of gradually getting the animals used to the observer's presence – a process called habituation.

In order to build upon the pioneering work of George Schaller and fill in the necessary details of gorilla behaviour and ecology, in 1967 Dr Louis Leakey promoted another research programme in the Virunga volcanoes, this time conducted by Dian Fossey. She, too, started at Kabara, but after the troubles which threw the Congo (now Zaire) into turmoil, she moved her camp a few kilometres eastward just inside Rwanda at the foot of Mt Visoke.

It was here that her persistence, determination, courage and hard work at last enabled her to habituate the gorillas to her presence and thereby make prolonged observations, at even closer range than Schaller. Professor Robert Hinde, a leading world authority on animal behaviour, who was supervising Jane Goodall's studies of chimpanzees, came to visit her and was so impressed by her work that he suggested that she should go to Cambridge and write up her findings. This meant, however, that if the camp were left unattended the three years' hard work spent in habituating four groups of gorillas could be lost. Dian's decision was to reshape my own future life and work, for she decided to go to Cambridge and therefore needed someone to continue research in the area of the camp. Just at this time I wrote to Professor Hinde enquiring about possible research projects and he passed my letter to Dian.

In retrospect, being interviewed by Dian, Professor Hinde and finally by Dr Leakey was less harrowing than the hectic months which followed. Soon my wife, Margaret, and I found that our whole lives were filled with letter writing, documentation, grant applications, passports and visas and all the mundane, but necessary, 'peripheral' activities to field research. In addition I still had to study for my final exams, and Margaret gave birth to our daughter Fiona! Finally, after six months of preparation, all our arrangements were complete and at last I was on my way to Africa.

Part One

RWANDA

CHAPTER ONE

Journey to the Virunga volcanoes

To get to Kigali, the capital of Rwanda, I had to break my journey in Nairobi. It proved to be a most inspiring stop-over, for I was able to stay with Dr Louis Leakey at his home at Langata just outside Nairobi. I found his enthusiasm for my proposed gorilla research, and indeed for any kind of field work, instantly infectious; he made one impatient to start, and my initial panic was completely forgotten. I looked forward to the day when I could show him the results of my work, but unfortunately, long before it was finished, Dr Leakey suddenly died.

At Kigali I was met by Dian Fossey and the photographer Bob Campbell. After spending only one night in the capital we left just after dawn the following morning and drove, or rather bounced uncomfortably, for over six hours along the unmade Rwandese roads. Eventually we crossed the border into Uganda at Cyanika and travelled on a few kilometres to Kisoro, where we bought supplies on a scale I had never imagined.

'Choose enough food to last for at least a month,' said Dian, 'for we do not come here frequently.' My mind boggled at thinking of so many meals in the space of a few minutes. I watched with amazement as the tins and packets I chose for thirty to forty breakfasts, and the same number of midday snacks and main evening meals, were piled upon the counter by an eager shop assistant, who obviously wanted to make sure that I did not starve. Soon the whole length of the twenty-five-foot counter was filled with the mounds of supplies which all three of us had chosen. Along the floor were cans of paraffin and methylated spirit for the cooking stoves and lamps at the camp.

Other assistants quickly packed our supplies and loaded them in our vehicle.

Eventually this mammoth task was completed and we drove, in darkness now, to the famous Traveller's Rest Hotel, once the unofficial 'gorilla headquarters' of the area. Walter Baumgärtel, the previous owner, had retired and gone home to Europe some years earlier but the new owner was keen to get gorilla safaris started again. Unfortunately gorilla sightings in the nearby saddle area between Mt Gahinga and Mt Muhavura were now very rare for the gorillas were getting fewer and fewer in the Ugandan section.

We retired early to bed and were up again at dawn. After breakfast we returned down the dusty road towards Rwanda, but this time we were going to turn off the main road and go up into the forested volcanoes, the nearest of which, Muhavura, now dominated the skyline and blocked our view to the north as we drove around its lower slopes. As so often happened at dawn there was no cloud cover: this would appear later in the day to shroud the entire peaks.

Just before we reached Ruhengeri, Bob turned the minibus (or 'kombie' as it is known in East Africa) into a side road and we travelled through dense stands of banana trees for a few hundred yards before emerging suddenly to see an amazing spectacle before us – the central Virunga volcanoes. 'That's Visoke,' said Bob, 'the smooth cone-shaped one. The one with the jagged peaks is Sabinio, and the very large one with the top still in cloud is Karisimbi, over fourteen thousand feet high.' The road got narrower, rougher and steeper as we slowly wound our way higher and higher. We travelled upwards for almost half an hour as I gazed in wonder at the incredible landscape all around me.

Suddenly we were overtaken by an African running frantically along the road. He was immediately followed by another and then another. We turned a corner and men working in the nearby fields dropped their tools and ran as though suddenly possessed. 'What on earth is happening?' I asked. We turned yet another bend and there in front of us was an enormous crowd of Rwandese, being joined every second by even more of

the running figures. 'Wapagazi' (porters), explained Dian. 'We
leave the kombie here and go on by foot, and these people want
the job of carrying our loads. There is little employment in this
area and it is very good pay for a few hours' work.' As we stopped
I thankfully stepped out among the excited jabbering crowd.
The final stage of my journey was about to start.

Willing hands quickly unloaded our many boxes of supplies.
With much excited chatter, good-natured laughter, and no
small amount of pushing and shoving, the porters eventually set
out the loads in line with a man behind each. With Guamhogazi, her head porter, Dian then checked that each load had
a porter and that each porter had a load. As she went along she
counted aloud in Swahili. 'Moja (one), mbili (two), tatu (three),
ine' (four) ... until she reached the end of the line ... 'makumi
tatu na ine' (thirty-four). It was almost like a scene from an
expedition of Livingstone, Burton or Stanley.

Eventually everyone was satisfied, except, of course, those
villagers who were not fortunate enough to get a load, and the
porters prepared to carry the heavy boxes in the traditional
manner. First they collected handfuls of nearby plants and
plaited them into a ring six inches in diameter, which they
placed on their head. Then, with the help of a friend, each
porter proceeded to balance his allotted load on this tiny
cushion. Their sense of balance was a delight to watch as each
man made minute adjustments to the position of his load so
that he could walk freely, without even the need to support it
with his hands. After much jovial complaining about the weight
of their own particular load (something which became a familiar
ritual on all subsequent occasions) the porters were finally
prepared for the climb up to Dian's camp.

'Tayari' (ready), shouted Dian. The cry rang back and forth
among the porters and the crowds of onlookers and our pro-
cession started. At that time the road itself ended near this
point, though it was later to be extended further up the mountain slopes for several miles. The porters followed a narrow track
which led uphill, passing through cultivated fields or 'shambas'.
Here the local Hutu population of Rwanda grew their crops of
beans, sorghum and sweet potatoes. In addition there were

patches of the newer crops which had been introduced by European agronomists: carrots, cabbages and peas and, most abundant of all, the white, daisy-like flowers of pyrethrum, the one plant which, as I learned later, was to affect so dramatically the whole ecology of the area.

We climbed on and on uphill. In parts the track was very steep, and for the first time some of the porters steadied their loads with one hand as they negotiated the more difficult sections. They strode easily up these slopes, continuously keeping up their chatter to each other back and forth along the line, with only their loud whistled exhalations giving any indication of the extra effort. I myself, after months of studying, was in fairly poor physical condition. At this altitude (2800 metres) it was all I could do to force my weary legs to carry my own body up the mountain, let alone carry an additional load of twenty kilos.

The cries of the porters changed to the local greeting in Kinyarwanda, their native language: 'Mraho' (Hello! How are you?), and answering cries soon rang back and forth. We were approaching a cluster of tiny, conical huts, each with an enlarged section of the thatched eaves overhanging the open doorway. Many of the local inhabitants were busily working in the nearby shambas, and the African hoe was being wielded in expert fashion by both men and women as they turned over the soil. Dian complained bitterly that this had all been part of the Volcano National Park until fairly recently, but under the auspices of a European development scheme some eight thousand hectares of this unique forest had been taken and cleared for agricultural purposes, mainly to grow pyrethrum. From this spot we could in fact see in the distance behind us the remains of the line of trees which had once been the park boundary.

Ahead and to the north-west we could see the slopes of Mt Visoke itself disappearing into the low-lying belt of mist and cloud. Dian's camp lay in the relatively flat, saddle-like area near a range of small hills which stretched almost from Mt Visoke to the nearby Mt Karisimbi. We could just see the top of the first of these hills above the forest ahead of us. As we climbed higher it became obvious that the attacks on the forest

22

were very recent and some large trees were standing amongst piles of smouldering undergrowth. The Rwandese were illustrating vividly how, as in so many parts of Africa, even the mighty jungle is soon vanquished by these age-old slash and burn techniques. We pressed on upwards and eventually reached the edge of the forest itself.

The track which had cut obliquely across the lower slopes of the volcano now turned sharply and headed directly uphill. Falling steeply away down to our right was an almost sheer drop into one of the many deep ravines which radiated from the summit of the volcano like the spokes of a giant cartwheel. In contrast to the sunlit open fields, filled with the cheerful workers who could still be heard shouting back and forth to each other behind us, the forest was dark, quiet, and to a foreigner like myself, somewhat menacing. The chatter of the porters increased as we entered its leafy shade. Many of them were virtual strangers to this other world above their homes. The more intrepid Hutu entered illegally to gather firewood, collect honey or to hunt for elephants and antelopes, but only the pygmoid Batwa felt really at home in the forest. All the local people thought that we were quite mad, not only to go and live there but to waste our time watching gorillas each day – an understandable sentiment and one shared even by some of my own family and friends!

We walked on and on through *Hagenia* forest for almost two hours, until suddenly we came out into a large, grassy and very boggy meadow. Across the other side, less than a hundred yards away, I saw two tiny green corrugated-iron cabins set amongst another clump of *Hagenia* trees. Plumes of smoke drifting lazily skywards reminded me that Dian called this 'Camp moshi' – camp of smoke. This then was the end of my safari, and after climbing to an altitude of 3050 metres to reach it, it appeared all the more heavenly. Each time I subsequently climbed the mountain it was always with an immense sense of relief, mixed with wonder, that I emerged from the forest to see the camp ahead.

A large orange-brown shape streaked towards us and I discovered that this was Cindy, Dian's boxer dog. Most of the porters were already at the camp and I could hear a lot of excited chatter and shouting as I approached. The cause of this excitement was Dian's other pet, a blue monkey called Kima. She was busy jumping from load to load as the porters filed into the camp. When they chased her away she clattered noisily across the corrugated-iron roof of the cabin and chattered angrily back at them.

The camp site was at the side of a small river which meandered through the saddle area between Mt Visoke and Mt Karisimbi. Around each cabin was a foot-deep ditch to carry away the deluge of the rainstorms, which were frequent at this altitude. In front of the larger cabin a small, rickety, plank table was placed at the side of a square pit in which burned a large log fire. On top of the logs were several smoke-blackened bowls full of water from the nearby stream. The fire-pit was ringed by a railing of saplings on which clothes were hopefully hanging to dry.

At the side of the fire-pit one of the camp workers was busily chopping firewood. Split logs were stacked neatly nearby and all around him were the chippings from countless days of wood cutting. A small moss-covered bridge crossed the bend in the river at this point and a path across it led to a large tent – Bob Campbell's home for some two years. A large flagpole, from which hung the red and yellow Rwandese flag, completed the scene. The setting was intimate and beautiful: the large umbrella shapes of the *Hagenia* trees gave a protective air to the camp, whilst the nearby meadow added a touch of openness. The swiftly flowing river, besides providing essential clean, fresh water, added just that touch of musical magic to complete the setting.

Meanwhile each porter had placed his load on the ground and was waiting expectantly. Dian went along the line giving each man one hundred francs (a mere fifty pence, or one dollar), and several cigarettes. However, since the only other work available to them was road building, which paid less than 25p (50 cents) a day to the lucky ones who were chosen, they were happy with their payment. Even after receiving his money each man remained behind his load. Dian told me afterwards that this was to prevent anyone who had already been paid from nipping smartly along to the end of the line to be paid yet again! After all the payments were made the porters were eager to be off down the mountain before dark. Amidst more laughter and shouts of farewell to the camp staff the porters literally raced off across the meadow like a crowd of schoolboys released from school. These men of the mountains had hardly noticed the stiff climb, despite their heavy loads.

Without the incessant chatter of the porters, camp was now strangely quiet. One of the men took my bags and led the way along one of the paths which radiated from the fire and there, some thirty yards away, stood the home in which I would live for the next eight months. It was an attractive little cabin which, although surfaced with corrugated iron, fitted in well with the forest because, like the others, it had been painted green. As I walked up the path I could see a large stone chimney on the side of the cabin nearest to me, capped by a chimney pot of metal tubing. On this side of the cabin the roof over half its length continued downwards, and under the extended eaves was a large kitchen-cum-store-room. The camp worker, whose name was Kanyuraguana, opened the door and took my bags inside. The cabin was partially divided into two rooms by a large plywood screen. The other walls were lined with a yellow-green matting made of fine grasses and the floor covering was of the same type, giving a restful colouring to the interior. The fireplace wall looked as though it had been made by a stone-craftsman. A log fire burned in a square hearth set among smooth volcanic rocks, neatly cemented together and shaped like a miniature pyramid. This was capped by a mantelpiece of fine dark wood. Above the fireplace was a painting so lifelike that I thought it was a photograph. It was by the American artist-naturalist Jay Matternes, well known for his drawings of prehistoric man; but this was of the animal I had travelled several thousand miles to see, the rare mountain gorilla.

In contrast to the simplicity of the cabin itself the furnishings were spartan and somewhat ugly. In the front room there was a long, rickety, wooden table and two tubular-metal, folding camp chairs. Behind the divider was a camp bed and a small camp table, the sum total of all the furniture. The light was now fading fast so I merely placed my suitcases and bags in the bedroom and went outside to examine the kitchen. It was about ten feet long and five feet wide with an open square window at the far end. Beneath the window was another small camp table on which was perched a double-burner paraffin stove. The floor, like the outside surroundings of the cabin itself, was covered with clean, black, volcanic gravel from the nearby river bed.

I heard someone coming up the path. It was Kanyuraguana carrying a hurricane lamp. He was followed by a couple of the men bringing more of my boxes of supplies. As yet my knowledge of Swahili was still very limited, so I merely indicated which boxes were to go in the outside store and which were to go inside the cabin. Kanyuraguana placed the hurricane lamp on the mantelpiece, then he added some more wood to the fire and blew expertly until cheerful flames sprang up to engulf the fresh logs. He obviously understood my inability to talk to him and I felt a great deal of frustration as I self-consciously mumbled 'Asanti' (Swahili for 'thank you'), to which he replied 'Ndio, Bwana' (Yes, Bwana).

As Kanyuraguana quietly closed the door behind him a feeling of utter inadequacy came over me. Here was I fresh from university with an honours degree, yet I could not even adequately perform the simplest of all human traits – communication with another human being. I looked forlornly into the fire, and listened to the hissing of the damp logs as the flames danced around them.

I went to bed early. The forest was quiet and I soon fell asleep, despite the fact that I could hardly wait for the morning when we would be setting off to see one of Dian's study groups.

CHAPTER TWO

On the gorilla trail

I was awakened by the sounds of Kanyuraguana leaving a bowl of hot water. I got up and washed and shaved in water that was so soft that it was slippery to the touch, then started to prepare breakfast. Meanwhile Kanyuraguana returned. 'Jambo, Bwana,' he murmured, '*chai*,' and handed me a flask containing my early morning tea. There was no end to the indispensability of this quiet, stockily built young man. Camp was never the same when Kanyuraguana went down the mountain to take his monthly spell of ten days' leave in his home village. Often he came back before his rest period was over. Whether it was because he was bored, or overworked at home, or because he needed his salary to save up for his own shamba, we never knew, but we were always glad to see him back at camp.

Soon after nine the Belgian Ambassador and his consul arrived with Guamhogazi, Dian's head porter, to see the gorillas which he was trying to protect through diplomatic channels. Kanyuraguana instantly produced yet another flask of *chai* which the visitors enjoyed whilst taking a short rest after their long climb. When they felt fit again Dian called out to her tracker, Nemeye, 'Tayari!' (ready) and his answering cry, 'Ndio' (yes), rang through the camp and into the surrounding forest. Each subsequent day spent at the camp was to begin with this short cheerful exchange before we went out on the gorilla trail.

The air was clear and chilly. With Nemeye and Munya, another tracker, leading, we followed the path which led past my cabin and continued westwards around the steep cone of Mt Visoke. This part of the saddle area appeared relatively flat, although in fact it sloped gently upwards in the direction we were taking. All around us were mature *Hagenia* trees, their bulbous, moss-padded branches covered with epiphytic ferns and orchids. We soon came to a bend in the river where the track crossed it near a clear, dark pool. Then the path climbed up from the river bed and led to another green, meadow-like area covered in grasses and sedges. At the side of the path was a massive cluster of daisy-like everlasting flowers (*Helichrysum*). These were in fact more frequent on the upper slopes of the mountains where the flowers and the upper leaf clusters of the plant were eaten by the gorillas. This particular large cluster brightened our morning walks for many a week until one day the flowers were all cut down and collected by a thoughtless tourist.

As I climbed up from the river the scene before my eyes was breathtakingly beautiful. Surrounding the meadow were *Hagenia* and *Hypericum* trees which were so covered with wisps of *Usnea* lichen that they looked as though they were decorated for a festive occasion. Even more striking were the two volcanic peaks which appeared to rise sheer from the forest itself. To our left was an enormous green cone, the upper third of which was sprinkled with white, like Mt Kilimanjaro or Mt Fujiyama. This was Mt Karisimbi, reaching 14,782 feet (4507 metres), the highest of the eight Virunga volcanoes. Straight ahead was another peak, Mt Mikeno, which at 14,553 feet (4437 metres) was the second highest peak. In many ways Mikeno was even more impressive than Karisimbi because its stark, bare rock face contrasted sharply with the forest beneath. The jagged twin peaks were the remains of the central volcanic plug of this extinct volcano; the crater rim had long since been eroded away. If Karisimbi was the Kilimanjaro of the Virunga volcanoes then Mikeno was surely the Eiger.

To our right rose the steep, forest-covered slopes of Mt Visoke and we ourselves stood in the relatively smooth saddle area between these massive peaks. I now understood how Carl Akeley had become captivated by the beauty of this remote region. It was indeed sad to think that he had died whilst attempting the first scientific study of the rare apes he had grown to admire and for whose future he himself was so concerned. His grave, at the edge of the Kabara meadow, lay just a few miles to the west of where we now stood, near where Mikeno appeared to rise out of the forest.

After taking in this idyllic scene we pressed on across the open meadow, and were brought sharply back to reality when we realized that much of the meadow was virtually a swamp. Large patches of *Sphagnum* mosses gave way beneath unwary feet to send us thigh deep in freezing cold water. In future I was to pay as much attention to where I was putting my feet as to the beautiful scenery, but in the rainy season it was almost impossible to keep dry, despite good quality mountain clothing. It was little wonder that Akeley had died of pneumonia in these conditions. At the far end of the meadow the track once more entered open *Hagenia* forest, then after a few minutes' walk we came upon our next natural hazard – giant nettles over six feet tall! Now was the time to put on the stout leather gloves which Dian had told me to bring from England. These were in fact excellent, but alas my jeans were no match for the nettles' virulent spikes and soon my legs were smarting from innumerable stings. Dian's tracker, Nemeye, a cheerful youth who was far more mature than his sixteen years, was in the lead with his older companion, Munya. Enthusiastically and expertly they wielded their sharp pangas like rapiers, first cutting the stems then pushing them aside all in one swift movement. Although this trail was used by someone from the camp almost daily the nettles were quick to grow or fall over the trail. Their tall spindly stems seemed to need the support of others to be stable; but upright or not their stings are far more virulent than their European counterparts.

Two hundred yards further on Nemeye mercifully led us uphill among the giant lobelias and out of the nettles. There was now no path save that cut by the trackers. The vegetation was still soaking wet from a combination of rain, dew and mist and this made walking very difficult, especially up steeper stretches. I clung to strands of herbs, vines and especially lobelia stems and as I struggled on I realized how inadequate was the human frame to negotiate such terrain. In order to clamber easily over this sort of vegetation one needed to have four legs instead of two, and ideally have feet that could grip like hands – in fact just like a gorilla! I reflected on how awkward the gorillas in zoos often appear: Robert Ardrey in his book *African Genesis* had described the shape of the gorilla as 'a sorry paradox of architectural incongruities'. Obviously, I thought, he had never tracked mountain gorillas in their own habitat. I laboured on, willing my so-called 'mountain boots' to become prehensile and stop sliding backwards at almost every pace.

After struggling uphill in this manner for about fifteen minutes we eventually found the trail of one of Dian's study groups which had passed this way the day before. Nemeye and Munya had seen them at this very place in the late afternoon, thus the gorillas must have slept not far from here. My heart beat faster; were we really that close? Was I really about to make my first contact with the gorillas? I had already been cautioned even as we left the cabin for speaking in a normal voice. Since human voices carried remarkable distances in the silence of the forest Dian told me that I would have to cultivate a lower pitched voice, rather like a loud whisper. Later, when I got used to it, this seemed to be the most natural way to talk in such quiet surroundings. But now, when on a fresh gorilla trail, even whispered comments were frowned upon, so we proceeded in silence.

Twenty minutes later we came upon an area where almost all the herbaceous vegetation had been flattened. Here and there were lobelias whose leafy tops had been decapitated, and sticky, latex-like sap hung in congealed trickles down their bare stems. This was the nest site, the place where the family group of gorillas had slept that night and which they had left just a few hours before we arrived.

It has long been known that gorillas make fresh nests each night and one can get a good idea of the age of the nests by examining the state of the vegetation from which they are made. In freshly made nests the leaves hang limp but are still green and moist. As time passes, however, they turn brown as they die. In older nests some of the vegetation will send out fresh shoots and leaves until eventually, after anything up to six months or more depending on the growth rate of the vegetation, the nest will be completely overgrown and hardly recognizable as such. Unfortunately the vagaries of the climatic conditions at these high altitudes can affect the vegetation so much that even an experienced observer could be misled when trying to estimate the age of some nests. Several consecutive days of mist and rain can keep trampled vegetation looking fairly fresh, while a few hours of tropical sun can make it appear several days old. If the gorillas nest in an area of lobelias the degree of coagulation of the sticky latex-like sap which exudes from their broken stems acts almost like an hour glass and gives a better indication of the age of the nests, though it, too, can be put out of time by the weather conditions.

Fortunately for us the gorillas leave other useful clues to enable the age of their nests to be estimated. Since they eat vast amounts of vegetable matter each day, much of which has a very high fibre content and is therefore almost impossible for non-ruminants like gorillas to digest, they eliminate large amounts of horse-like dung each day and night. The dung consists of masses of partially digested and undigested plant remains usually deposited in distinctive lobes, the size of which gives a clear indication of the size of the gorilla who left it. Since some of the longer plant fibres are continuous throughout the lobes these tend to keep them together rather like a string of beads. Fresh dung is a uniform colour but quickly discolours underneath as the moisture content runs out. Unfortunately, however, even the appearance of the dung is often markedly influenced by the weather conditions and dung in nearby nests can appear to be of different ages if one nest is sheltered while the other is fully exposed to the elements. Also, to complicate matters even further, the gorillas of the Virunga region usually deposit their dung inside their nests and then proceed to squash the lobes flat when they sleep on it!

The dung gives another important clue in helping to decide whether it is fresh or not. Schaller had noted that, often within minutes of the dung being deposited, flies begin to lay clusters of tiny white eggs on its outer surface. First the lobes of gorilla dung have just a few clusters of eggs, soon all have an almost completely white bloom.

A combination of clues from many signs such as these gives

an experienced observer much accurate information not only about the age of the nest site but about the numbers and composition of the group; their recent diet as indicated in their dung; the general state of their health by its physical state and the presence or absence of intestinal parasites. It may also be possible to infer some social relations within the group by mapping the location of each member on consecutive nights over prolonged periods, though this is fraught with many procedural difficulties. However, the location of certain group members, particularly the adult silverbacked males, is easy to find, for one has only to look for the largest nest and the largest of the lobes, usually over three inches in diameter.

Dian pointed out where the one silverback of this group had slept. A few yards away was a nest which contained not only lobes of dung some two to three inches in diameter, but a further five tiny lobes each barely one inch wide. This was the nest of an adult female and her infant, for until they are about three years old the infants sleep close by their mother's side in her nest.

While Dian had been showing us some of the features of the nest site Nemeye and Munya had found the trail left by the gorilla group when they vacated their nests a few hours earlier. From the number of nests counted in all, their approximate composition and the location of the nest site on the south-west slopes of Mt Visoke, Dian thought that we were on the trail of the study group which she knew as Group 9 (the number being its order of discovery since she began her study). Groups 1, 2 and 3 were over near Kabara, and therefore outside the Visoke study area. However, Group 4 also used these slopes and had a similar composition to Group 9. We would soon know on contacting the group, for each was led by its own adult silverback, Group 4 by a placid male whom Dian had affectionately named Uncle Bert, and Group 9 by another silverback rather disturbingly named Geronimo!

Having rested while the trackers counted the nests we set off refreshed, knowing that the trail we were following now led not to another nest site, as it would have if the original trail had been several days old, but to the gorillas themselves. Nemeye and Munya led the way, followed by Dian and the Ambassador and his consul, while Bob and I brought up the rear. The trail first went uphill and soon we reached a natural track running along one of the many ridges. I was hardly surprised to see elephant and buffalo signs on this track as George Schaller had noted that they climb even to the very summit of Visoke, over twelve thousand feet. Suddenly the gorilla trail, for no apparent reason, turned down into the ravine which dropped sharply to our left. We all slithered, slipped and partially fell down the wet slope. Then, after negotiating a muddy trickle which ran down the centre of the ravine from its source way above our heads on the cloudy upper slopes, we scrambled up the other side. We struggled on for another hour, crossing several more ravines. Then just after midday the trail turned downhill again. Ahead of us Nemeye was anxiously pointing out some gorilla dung to Dian. Bob Campbell whispered to me that the group had passed this way very recently and in fact might be resting nearby. As we passed the dung I could see that it bore only a few of the tiny white eggs of the dung flies. But more exciting even than this, as I touched the dung lightly with the backs of my fingers, I noticed that unlike the dung in the nests this was still warm. We now had to proceed very slowly, cautiously and as silently as possible in order to try and hear the gorillas before they heard us. Nemeye now used his sharp panga not as a flashing rapier but as a lever to lift vegetation gingerly aside as we quietly crept down the ridge path. Despite our snail-like pace my heart was thumping faster than ever as I anticipated the screams and the inevitable charge of the adult male which would occur when we made contact with the group.

After ten minutes of creeping quietly downhill our little caravan stopped and Bob signalled me to keep very still and listen carefully. Over to our left amongst the dense vegetation in a shallow ravine I heard some gentle movements in the vegetation, scarcely audible even in the quiet mountain air. I looked at Bob, who smiled and nodded. We had found them at last. After a whispered discussion ahead we continued downhill carefully threading our way through the litter of dead twigs, which tended to crack like pistol shots under careless feet. Fifty yards further on Dian knelt down and carefully started to part the vegetation on the left-hand side of the track. She motioned for all of us to kneel down and then we slowly continued in single file. Nemeye and Munya, their tracking work now over, sat out of sight behind some shrubs. They smiled reassuringly as I crept past, but I wondered what they really thought of our expedition. Ten yards further on Bob signalled me to stop once more. While the four of us watched, Dian quietly crept forward by herself. Suddenly a gentle slapping sound, which I recognized as a chest-beat, rang out, probably from a juvenile or young adult since it did not have the deep powerful resonance of an adult animal. Dian immediately stopped moving and then gently slapped her gloved hands alternately against her thigh in an imitation of the chest-beat. She later explained that this often makes the gorillas curious and they then come forward to see what it is that is making such a noise. For she stressed that when you are near a gorilla group it is most important to let the gorillas come forward to you and not for you to keep on going towards the gorillas, since this could be interpreted by them as a threatening attitude and might cause them to flee – or possibly to retaliate with a charge or even an attack if threatened sufficiently.

Immediately Dian had finished her imitation chest-beat, a strange cry rang out, 'Uh-uh-u?' Dian smiled, for this gentle vocalization, which she called a questioning bark since the intonation really gave the impression of 'Who are you?' indicated a friendly contact with one of her four habituated study groups. The reaction of an unhabituated group, I was later to learn, is usually more vociferous, often violent and unpredictable. So also was that of the habituated Group 8, an unusual group which consisted of only five bachelor males with whom I was later to have several memorable contacts.

Although this type of questioning vocalization is given by gorillas of all groups, especially adult males, Dian recognized this to be from Geronimo, the leader of her study Group 9. She began to pull at some of the nearby vegetation, gently breaking, twisting and tearing off leaves, thereby imitating a feeding animal. Loud lip-smacking was also thrown in to give a realistic impression of a contented gorilla, peacefully feeding and showing no antagonistic intentions. Another gentle chest-beat rang out and Dian immediately replied with a similar sound, this time by gently slapping her gloved hands together so that it sounded more like an infant gorilla than an adult.

Bob had joined in the simulated feeding behaviour and was busy crushing the hollow stems of wild celery and then running his clenched fingers along thistle stems, thereby stripping off the leaves with loud tearing sounds. The rest of us joined in until I was sure we sounded more like a herd of feeding elephants than a small family of gorillas. Dian was inching her way forward, still in a kneeling position. Since it was impossible to see over the dense, six-foot-high ground cover, she quietly pushed it to one side as she slowly progressed. Another 'Uh-uh-u?' rang out and this time Dian replied with gentle baby-like vocalizations of 'Na-o-ome, na-o-ome'. Suddenly a loud penetrating 'Pok-a-pok-a-pok-a-pok-a-pok' rang out shattering the peace of the forest as the adult male gave his warning chest-beat. Dian stopped creeping forward and proceeded to 'feed' once more on the nearby vegetation, even putting some of the leaves in her mouth while pretending to eat them. After a few more minutes of this she inched her way forward again until she could see uphill round a small bush. She paused and repeated her feeding behaviour interspersed with more baby-like vocalization. After five minutes or so she motioned for the Ambassador to creep slowly forward. He did so enthusiastically, and another loud 'Pok-a-pok-a-pok' chest-beat rang out. Dian frowned and sig-nalled for him to pause and then proceed more slowly and carefully. As he reached her side I could see from the surprised yet pleased look on his face that the animals which he had tried so hard to protect at Government level were at last in his sight. His consul was next to creep eagerly forward and I awaited my turn to join them. At last, like an overgrown mouse, I crept forward to see my study animal for the first time in its natural habitat.

Although I had read the detailed descriptions of George Schaller, seen Bob Campbell's excellent colour photographs and seen gorillas in zoos, the animal now before me was even

35

more impressive than I had been able to imagine. His long powerful arms and short, stocky legs supported a barrel-shaped body. Contrasting sharply with the long, jet-black hairs on his shoulders and arms, the hairs on the broad band of his back and rump were the shining silver-grey of a fully mature adult male – a real silverback. He was magnificent. His physique was so apparently well suited to his life in these forests that Ardrey's description now became laughable. 'That's Geronimo,' whispered Dian, 'the silverback leader of Group 9. Look at the hair above his eyes and you will see why I called him Geronimo, but be careful to move very slowly and *do not* stare directly into his eyes, especially with binoculars, for they do not like to be stared at.'

As we watched him Geronimo sat down slowly. He reached out with his right hand, curving his enormous fingers around the upper stem of a nearby thistle, just as Bob Campbell had done a few minutes earlier. Then, by sliding his clenched hand quickly up to the top of the stem he removed the upper leaves, but, unlike Bob, he popped the spiky bundle into his mouth and chewed away as though they were as tender and as smooth as lettuce leaves! Even while he was chewing he was busy giving another nearby thistle plant similar treatment, this time merely stripping off the outer two-thirds of the leaf blade from one of the foot-long leaves leaving the petiole intact but bare. I slowly raised my binoculars and examined his face, starting with the enormous, protruding jaws and a mouth full of teeth blackened by a tartar covering. The bright pink tongue seemed oblivious to the thistle spikes. Geronimo's nose was, as in all gorillas, squat and flattened, but his nostrils were flared and surrounded by neat, heart-shaped fleshy ridges, black and shiny as coal. A fluted nasal ridge was topped by two deeply set brown eyes which, even through binoculars and from this distance, were penetrating and captivating. I recalled the penetrating eyes of the stuffed specimen which I had seen in the National Museum in Nairobi, but those of Geronimo had that extra magical sparkle of vitality and life. Protruding brow ridges were tightly puckered as though he were permanently frowning. The tufted mass of short, bristly hair on his forehead contrasted sharply with the black, hairless shiny skin on his face. And here, rather than in any ferocious aspect of his behaviour, was surely the reason for his name. A large triangular patch of the hair on his forehead was a bright, reddish-brown colour and looked just like the war-like markings of a tribal chief. His head rose sharply upwards from his eyebrows in a curious conical shape and was capped by tufty spiky hair, also with a reddish tinge. As I watched I saw this strange conical top to his head bulging and moving. Recalling the lectures on primate anatomy that I had received I tried to visualize the shape of the skull beneath that bulging cone.

The massive protruding jaws of gorillas, which they use to tear off strips of bark or to crush stout plant stems so easily, need powerful muscles to operate such large levers. These are particularly enormous in adult males and the muscles are attached to the lateral surfaces of the skull at their upper endings. Our own jaws are moved in a similar manner and the action of the muscles can easily be felt during vigorous chewing. Whilst our relatively puny musculature finds enough surface area for attachment on the parietal and temporal sides of our skull, this surface area is far too small for the much larger muscles required to move the enormous jaws of adult male gorillas. As the animal grows, therefore, and the muscles gradually increase in size, they induce the top of the skull to protrude into a bony crest – the so-called parietal crest. This can clearly be seen on the skulls of adult male gorillas in museum collections. The bulging muscles along this crest and a further set at right angles to it, located above and behind the ears, the nuchal crest, made Geronimo look as though he was wearing a bishop's mitre.

Apparently unperturbed by our presence, he carried on feeding. The next item to go into the cavernous mouth was a large piece of the stem of a wild celery plant which he snapped off as though the inch-wide stem was a mere dandelion. Then, with beautifully co-ordinated action of hands, teeth and jaws he stripped off the coarse, outer covering to expose the hollow, tubular, white stem from which he contentedly bit off large pieces.

A movement at his side caught my eye and I stared at the vegetation through my binoculars. The diminutive roundish face of a juvenile peered cheekily above some brambles and then popped down again. How tiny it looked compared to the gargantuan figure of Geronimo, who must easily have weighed over three hundred pounds. My eyes scanned the darkness of the vegetation for other members of the group and I made a note of the animals I saw: one silverback, three adults (two probably females and the third possibly a sub-adult male), one adult female with a tiny infant – perhaps the one whose dung we found in the night nest, another male much smaller than Geronimo and lacking his silver 'saddle' (therefore referred to as a 'blackback') and one young juvenile. Dian had told me that by constantly checking the night nests and comparing the counts with visual sightings she had been able to find out the precise composition of each of her four study groups. In this way one could then monitor changes due to births, deaths, or emigrations and immigrations if these took place.

The female with the infant, which was probably less than a year old, was lying on her side among a flattened patch of herbs and vines which I later discovered was a casually made 'day nest' – as opposed to the nests used for sleeping in, or night nests. She was staring intently in our direction, then she looked at Geronimo, then back at us and then back at him as though to say 'What are you going to do about them?' Fortunately he was too engrossed in his snack of thistles and wild celery to bother with the subservient white apes who made lots of feeding noises without actually eating anything.

The infant nibbled at its mother's arm and she immediately rolled over and opened her mouth wide to bite. My heart sank as her large mouth almost engulfed the tiny arm of her offspring. But instead of the expected screams the infant 'chuckled' and easily wriggled free. It ran away a yard or so, paused, then charged back to pounce playfully upon its mother. Once again she opened her mouth, although I noticed this time that it was by no means wide open, and growling gently she clutched her infant with both arms. She then proceeded to mouth the squirming bundle in a form of 'play-biting' all over its body. After a few minutes of such hectic treatment the infant had obviously had enough for it wriggled free then lay quietly just out of arm's reach. The other members of the group appeared to be taking their midday siesta. Geronimo, too, had apparently satisfied even his barrel-sized stomach and was now lying on his back. His enormous jaws were sticking right up in the air like some gigantic rounded beak. From this angle he appeared to have a short, whiskery beard which made him look like a comical, fat old man taking a nap in his local park. It was all a peaceful domestic scene which I felt really privileged to be watching.

After resting for over thirty minutes Geronimo suddenly rolled over and stood up. A mixed look of annoyance and bewilderment came over his face as though he had just woken up from a dream and was wondering where we had suddenly appeared from. I was later to see the same sort of behaviour shown by Uncle Bert, the silverback of Group 4. It was as if they drifted off into a carefree, relaxed sleep and then suddenly woke up to find, or remember, that intruders were nearby. After standing motionless for a full minute Geronimo turned and walked majestically and purposefully off uphill. The other members of the group followed immediately. The tiny infant had climbed up on to its mother's back and was riding jockey-style as she strode uphill.

Whenever I got close to habituated gorillas in future I always felt, as on this occasion, a strong bond between us. Their deep brown eyes, often almost piercing golden orange in bright sunlight, reflected a mixed feeling of curiosity and trust, tinged with a little fear and respect. I could only conclude that my own eyes and face reflected a similar feeling. However, as they watched intently while I wrote down notes on their behaviour I could never escape the feeling that I, too, was the subject of close, intelligent scrutiny and that all my actions were being recorded, catalogued and interpreted! It was a most wonderful feeling to realize that, by not attacking me or running away, these animals were giving me the highest privilege they could –

39

their trust and acceptance. I paid sincere tribute to the small band of dedicated people who had made this trust possible; to the pioneering work of Akeley, who had initiated the setting up of this gorilla sanctuary; to the painstaking, detailed scientific work of George Schaller, who was the first to really show that these 'wild' gorillas could be habituated to man; and finally to Dian, who was extending Schaller's techniques with such obvious success.

With a feeling of elation, yet sadness that this wonderful contact was over, I followed our party as we prepared to leave. Fortunately Nemeye and Munya knew this place well and so they were able to lead us directly down the ridge track, where we soon reached the continuation of the path we had left in the nettle field just a few hours earlier – or was it a lifetime? Even the nettles seemed to have lost their sting as we thoughtfully retraced our steps back to camp. Everything now seemed strange, as though the forest on the mountain above had enabled us to step through some magical barrier into another world, the peaceful world of the mountain gorilla, and, having glimpsed some fascinating aspects of his daily life we suddenly had to return to our own, which would now never be quite the same. Even after many subsequent contacts with these gorillas I could never escape the somewhat empty, unreal sensations which I felt when all sound of the group faded away and the forest was once more quiet and still. It was as if one had, in a dream, travelled to a strange country only to wake up before the dream was ended and then try desperately and unsuccessfully to go back to sleep and return. As if to heighten the dream-like quality, the nearby peaks of Karisimbi, Mikeno, and Visoke itself, slowly disappeared behind a white wall of mist and cloud. Soon it swirled even lower, and finally engulfed the forest, the meadow and ourselves in its intangible whiteness.

At camp the Ambassador and his consul thanked Dian and quickly said goodbye, for they wanted to be down the mountain before the inevitable rain started. They were returning to Europe next day and promised to try and ensure the vital international support which was needed for the conservation of the mountain gorilla and its unique habitat. They were obviously excited about the tales they would be able to tell their friends and families about the day they spent with the gorillas of Visoke. I, too, was excited but, unlike them, I was not returning down the mountain. This camp was to be my home for some time to come.

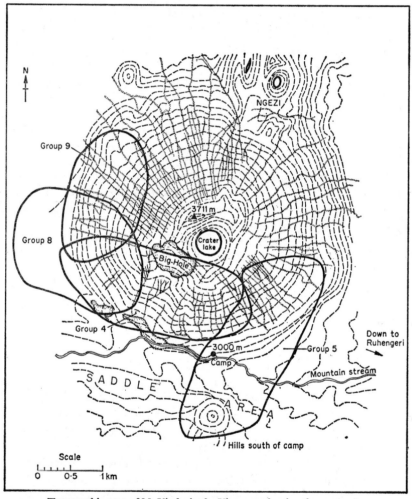

Topographic map of Mt Visoke in the Virungas, showing the many ravines radiating around the cone (the home range areas of groups 4, 5, 8 and 9 are shown in heavy outline).

CHAPTER THREE

Frustrations and rewards

Dian's departure to Cambridge was imminent. She still had work to complete, and I had a lot to learn before she left camp, so most of the next ten days was spent in tracking the gorillas. Unfortunately, although I had so much to learn about the techniques of observing the study groups, other considerations had to take priority at this time. Bob Campbell had to take more pictures of Dian close to the gorillas. These were required by her sponsors, the National Geographic Society, for it was primarily with funds from this society that the camp was financed. Often, while the gorillas were being filmed on one side of a bush I had to hide out of sight on the other, and consequently I saw relatively little of them.

There were other frustrations which were incidental to the gorilla research. One morning, after travelling only a short distance from camp, Nemeye stopped abruptly and pointed ahead. I looked through my binoculars half expecting to see gorillas, or at least an antelope. I could hardly believe my eyes. There before me, as though on a farm and not in a National Park, were dozens of cows! Dian was furious and after a short discussion decided to abandon the day's gorilla tracking. Instead we were to drive the cattle over into the Zaire side of the border. As George Schaller had found ten years earlier, the guards in Zaire were far more stringent than in Rwanda. Dian believed that anyone having cows illegally in the park was more likely to be caught if they were on that side of the border, hence the idea of the cattle drive.

Returning briefly to camp we collected two more of the men before we set out on our cattle round-up. When we reached the large meadow we saw well over a hundred cows, and here, scattered on and around the meadow, were easily another hundred. Such a herd can cause a great deal of damage in a few days by browsing and by the devastating trampling effect of such large numbers, especially when combined with the cutting of many saplings and side branches of small trees by their herders to provide the scrawny cattle with sufficient forage.

As we drove the cows across the meadow one of them unfortunately got itself stuck in a boggy patch. It struggled violently and eventually managed to free itself. As it hobbled away I was horrified to see that during its frantic struggles it had broken a foreleg. Although Bob had his rifle it would have been unwise to shoot a cow in the Rwandese section of the park. The unfortunate animal was therefore allowed to hobble on after the rest of the herd, and surprisingly it kept up with them.

Driving cattle across open meadows is relatively easy. Even an inexperienced cowhand like myself can wield a stick to any cow with wanderlust and thus keep the herd travelling in one direction. But trying to drive a herd of some two hundred cattle along a winding trail in mountain forest is like trying to herd the fleas on a dog's back! Once in the forest the cows became individualists and chose their own direction – which was anywhere but where we wanted them to go. We were constantly trying to head off break-away groups and keep them all going towards Zaire and away from Rwanda. It was exhausting and frustrating work and our herd kept dwindling in size as we travelled on. While I stood watching some ten cows rushing off in as many different directions Dian shouted caustically that I wasn't much use 'sitting on my butt', as she put it, and to 'make myself useful and bring them back'. Feeling annoyed and somewhat bewildered by the thought of trying to surround ten renegade cows single-handed I rushed off to try and redeem myself. I managed to return only two and hoped that Dian wasn't looking.

We struggled on, driving our dwindling herd over the unmarked border and also deeper into Zaire. On our way we found many traps which had been set by poachers to capture antelopes. These were either destroyed or collected by Dian's men. Dian told me that the local Watutsi had the region divided into sections, each for the use of a particular herder and his herd, and that she had already had several confrontations with this particular individual whose 'home range' happened to cover her study area. This time she hoped that his cows would be confiscated by the Zaire authorities.

We continued our cattle drive for another hour until Dian considered that we had driven them sufficiently deep into Zaire territory. We then thankfully left our reluctant herd and slowly returned to camp, keeping watch for the herder, who, however, was keeping well hidden. As we wandered back I began to think over our day's work and wondered what right we, as outsiders, had to interfere in this situation. I later learned that the Zaire guards only very rarely entered this section of the park, since it was cold, wet and far from their homes. Therefore the cattle herder probably merely collected his lead cow, and with her rattling bell and his reassuring voice, soon gathered up his scattered herd to take them back into Rwanda. Similarly the poachers would return to set new traps. Had I come to Africa to chase poachers and cattle, to be a free-lance people-fighter in a land I knew so little about?

The next two days were spent trying to contact Group 4 but on both occasions the contacts were very brief and yielded little in the way of observations due to extremely heavy rain and mist. On the following day we were fortunate enough to contact the group before the rain began. Once more Dian and Bob crept forward to try to get some close-up pictures while I sat on a fallen tree some ten yards back along the track. Hardly had I sat down when a sudden gust of wind blew up from nowhere, bringing with it wisps of mist so tenuous that they did not seem real. However, their reality was soon in no doubt as a white wall of mist advanced over the forest sending flickering fingers ahead like some giant amoeba feeling its way. Suddenly we were engulfed in its whiteness, which then grew darker and darker every second. A distant noise seemed to be getting nearer and louder and then a slap, slap, slap on the nearby leaves made me realize that the noise was not a herd of approaching elephants but the thunder of torrential rain. As I pushed my way into the vines which were growing around the fallen tree the downpour reached us and swept on in its relentless journey. I was glad I had good mountain clothing, though my waterproof nylon jacket was back at camp and I only had with me a proofed cotton anorak.

I sat despondently for two hours as the rain fell without a hint of reprieve. Then, not wishing to share the same fate as Akeley and others who had died of pneumonia, I decided to return to camp. Since Dian and Bob were huddled under their waterproofs but a few yards from Group 4 (the gorillas would also be huddled over in such rain, relying on their long black hair to keep them warm), I could hardly go and tell them of my departure. I therefore wrote them a brief note and spiked it securely to a prominent branch on the trail. I soon reached the main track which led down the ridge, made by elephants it was in fact called the 'Elephant Trail' by Dian and her trackers. When we had climbed up in the morning we had seen the clear footprints of elephants still full of water. Now, after over two hours of rain on the fine volcanic soil the track became a veritable river as the enormous run-off from the forest found the easiest course downhill. I came down the trail in a style partly of a scree-runner, partly of an inexperienced skier, decidedly undignified but rapid. In ten minutes I was in the saddle area. Another fifteen and I was walking back into camp shouting for hot water and hearing Kanyuraguana's cheerful and reassuring 'Ndio, Bwana'. Dian and Bob returned half an hour later and squelched past my door. They, too, had given up when it became obvious that the rainstorm was not going to cease for many hours.

Darkness fell early on such stormy days so I wrote up my notes and reports by the light of a hurricane lamp. I then set about preparing myself a meal. It had seemed strange to me that here, ten thousand feet up on a volcano, were living three people, each cooking his own meal and then eating it in the silence of his own cabin. After the pressures of my exams I had been looking forward to some discussions about biological principles and research, particularly on gorillas. Yet here I was as isolated now as one is in an examination hall, surrounded by others yet unable to communicate with them. I began to think about my situation, and I seemed to be sucked into a downward spiral of severe depression.

Never before had I experienced such depression and I was unprepared for this situation. I felt more and more sorry for myself. I seemed to be so much out of my element. Why had I got into a situation which took me so far from my family and all familiar things? I should be at home in England with my wife, Margaret, and our newly born daughter. Why was I, a teacher, trying to study the behaviour of wild gorillas? Indeed, *which* aspect of their behaviour was I going to study? Surely it must all be a terrible mistake!

As I reached the bottom of the spiral I decided that there was only one way to climb back up to sanity. Despite the expense, the complications and the ignominy, I would have to return home. But how would Dian take this, for tomorrow she herself would be setting off home to California before going to Cambridge? Several others before me had given up and she and Dr Leakey had been sure that I, as an older and more mature person, could cope with the difficulties of this remote life. Unfortunately depression respects no boundaries of maturity and strikes just as hard and relentlessly at any age. I hated defeat, but eventually I went down to Dian's cabin to tell her of my decision to return home.

Dian was finishing her packing. Although I tried to act normally she saw immediately that something was drastically wrong. She listened sympathetically to my tale of woe before telling me that she, too, had been very depressed when she first started her study three years earlier. She recalled that when her friend Alyette de Munck left her alone on the mountain for the first time she had run and locked herself in her cabin when one of the African camp staff came to speak to her. Later, upon translating his words with the aid of her *Upcountry Swahili* book, she had discovered that he had merely asked her if she required some hot water! Such is the fear of the unknown. I had felt that my fear was real enough, but Dian insisted that once she had left and I would not have her 'bitching at me', as she put it, I would feel better. She had asked the National Geographic to recall Bob and he, too, would be leaving shortly after her. 'Once you are on your own,' she said, 'running the camp by yourself and going out to do your own study, you will be fine. Then before you know it it will be time for Margaret and Fiona to come out and join you.' Somewhat reluctantly I rationalized the situation and finally agreed to stay. When she left early the next morning I did not feel as depressed as I had expected and did not wish too desperately to change places with her as she crossed the meadow and disappeared into the *Hagenia* forest on her way home.

Dian was right. Once she had left and I had to cope by myself I soon became absorbed by the work with the gorillas and the responsibilities of running the camp. In the meantime Bob was trying to complete his photographic work on the gorillas by concentrating his attention on the nearby Group 4. I contacted some of the other groups and tried to familiarize myself both with the study area and with the broad pattern of the behaviour of the gorillas. I tried to choose some aspects which I could realistically and usefully study in more detail for my PhD project. Several times Bob joined me and we contacted Group 5, which had two mature silverbacks within the group and a third which had recently become a peripheral. Dian had named these three Beethoven, Bartok and Brahms. I gratefully learned more about the habituation techniques from Bob and enjoyed my days in the field in his quiet and congenial company.

Apparently the secret of successful habituation was indeed to pretend to be an inoffensive fellow primate contentedly and peacefully feeding, no more threatening than the squirrels, birds or antelopes which the gorillas see every day. The ground cover of herbs and vines was usually six to eight feet high and often very dense. Dian believed that a small figure posed less of a threat to the gorillas and therefore both she and Bob always sat or knelt down when near the gorillas. The restrictions that this imposed on contact depended upon the nature of the terrain at that point and the relative positions of the gorillas and the observer. If the terrain was fairly flat then the gorillas had to be within a few yards before they could be seen clearly. Dian had therefore evolved techniques which played upon their natural curiosity. By encouraging the gorillas to come towards her this enabled her to see them. She did this by imitating their own feeding noises, vocalizations and even chest-beats, though all in a gentle, toned-down form to signify peaceful and harmless intentions. With the use of these techniques she eventually got Peanuts, one of the young males in Group 8, to take a small *Pygeum* fruit from her hand. During the weeks that followed Dian's departure I was never able to encourage the gorillas to come that close to me. They were obviously quite capable of recognizing that I was somehow different, and as yet I was not to be given the same degree of trust.

After Bob left at the end of August, I continued my day-to-day search for the gorillas and made several contacts with the study groups. On each occasion I tried to make notes on all aspects of their behaviour which I later transcribed under various headings such as grooming, play, feeding, vocalization, etc. Unfortunately the gorillas were often in areas of dense vegetation, which restricted my observations. Such was the situation one particular day when I contacted Group 4. It seemed as though I was again only going to get obscured views of them.

They were resting among thick vegetation on a narrow ridge. Unfortunately their trail had led me to a spot on a nearby ridge which, although very close, was lower than their resting place. I could only catch glimpses of the animals when they occasionally changed their resting positions. They had obviously already built their midday nests and were well settled in after a morning spent feeding.

Apart from a single alarm bark from Uncle Bert, the mature silverback leader of the group, they were very quiet. I therefore decided to try and circle round them to get to a better vantage point. Unfortunately, I was in clear view and as soon as I moved Uncle Bert was on his feet giving another loud alarm bark. I quickly sat down again and began to 'eat' some nearby vegetation and scratch casually as though nothing was amiss. Uncle Bert glared down in my direction for another five minutes, then after giving a rapid 'pok-a-pok-a-pok-a-pok-a-pok' chest-beat, he sat down again. He gave a perfect demonstration of how the adult males are able to produce their deep resonating chest-beats. Their pectoral muscles are so large and taut that two 'pockets' are formed beneath them, one on either side; thus by striking here with slightly cupped hands the air is trapped – as in clapping with cupped hands. Younger males, and more flabby-chested females, are therefore not able to produce quite such a clear sound.

I waited for a full half-hour before I attempted to move again. This time I literally inched my way backwards, but in the stillness of the forest even such tiny movements are not secret for long. I had gone but a yard before Uncle Bert was on his feet once more. His alarm call this time was louder and was followed by a short charge in my direction. Rather euphemistically this type of charge is referred to as a 'foliage run'. His intentions, however, were clear. Either I stayed still, or else! Therefore I stayed still.

Once more Uncle Bert lay down in his day nest. I could now see that his head was not fully lowered to the ground. He must have been resting his enormous chin on his folded arms, thereby keeping a wary eye on my every move. 'How he will curse me if the sun comes out,' I thought, for I had once seen him lying flat on his back, arms outstretched, as though worshipping the rare visit of the sun god to these mist-covered slopes. Each time the sun had been obscured by a passing cloud his mighty, hairy arms had closed over his hairless chest, to open again immediately the sun reappeared! However, today was typically dull and gloomy. No doubt when their rest period was over Uncle Bert would lead the group away and that would be the end of a fruitless contact. I cursed my luck.

The group rested in their obscured position for a further forty minutes then suddenly, as though on a signal, they all rushed down the slope, not away from me as I had expected, but towards me! I had gradually been easing myself into a comfortable position among the dead leaves and matted vegetation on the stump of a long-fallen *Hagenia* tree. By now it was like a large armchair so there I sat, transfixed, as though sitting watching a film, as the group members walked, tumbled, rolled or slid towards the bottom of the shallow ravine which separated us. Not a single vocalization was given and I had not seen who initiated this apparent charge. 'Surely they cannot be coming to take it out on me as a group? Gorillas are not supposed to do that sort of thing,' I said to myself reassuringly, though somewhat uncertainly. I could not see all the group members because of the dense vegetation. I quickly counted those I could see: the silverback, two young adults, three infants, two adult females and, to my great surprise and delight, a third adult female clutching a new baby in the crook of her right arm.

To my intense relief the group did not head directly up the near side of the ravine towards me, but followed a path which took them slightly higher up the slope. As he reached a spot some five or six metres immediately above me Uncle Bert paused. Slowly and majestically he turned his head to look down at me with his penetrating brown eyes. I had the strange feeling that this was an intelligent creature carefully observing me and noting my own behaviour. I tried to will my peaceful intentions to him across the immense evolutionary gulf separating our species. As though carved from the nearby volcanic rock he stood there motionless for what seemed an eternity. 'Is he deciding whether to attack, to scare or just to impress me?' I thought. I recalled my training in animal behaviour and tried, rather unsuccessfully, not to be so anthropomorphic.

Without a single vocalization, chest-beat or other display Uncle Bert turned his head and walked on. Several of the group, including the female with the baby, had already passed by higher up the slope. However, two young adults were nearer to me than Uncle Bert, and apparently were not in such a hurry. I recognized one of them as Bravado, for two of the toes on her left foot were joined together as I had seen in the photographs which Dian had left me. She sat down nonchalantly only four metres away and began to strip the upper leaves from a nearby thistle plant. I again marvelled at the ease with which the gorilla's leathery hands overcame the many spikes, and the apparently insensitive reaction of the pink tongue. Another young adult whom Dian had named Macho (meaning 'eyes' in Swahili) approached Bravado. With scarcely a pause in her feeding, Bravado gave a series of 'pants' or 'pig-grunts' as Macho approached. Bravado's chest rose and fell rapidly and her lips were slightly parted, the vocalization coming from deep within her throat and chest. Macho immediately circled around the seated Bravado and found another patch of thistles higher up the slope.

This then was a clear-cut interaction between two similarly-aged young adults. The one already in possession of a feeding patch had given a specific vocalization, a series of pig-grunts, on the approach of the other, who had then moved away to feed elsewhere.

Although simple by human standards gorilla communication is relatively complex and consists of a series of some twenty auditory, visual and even chemical signals. Some of these are long-range signals, such as the chest-beating of mature males, and apparently serve to keep each group leader aware of the positions of nearby groups and so help to keep them apart. Others, such as the pig-grunting, are close-range signals given between individuals within a group and these keep group members informed about one another's intentions. Each vocalization may mean little on its own but has to be viewed in relation to the general situation, such as who gives it and who receives it, where and when it is given, and whether any accompanying postural or chemical signals are given. The signals obviously mean more to the gorillas than human observers can ever appreciate, for we cannot transpose ourselves into their whole stimulus situation. For example, an arm wave given by humans may be interpreted as friendly or aggressive depending upon both the general situation in which it occurs and the specific parts of the action, such as fingers open or clenched, and the accompanying acts, such as facial smile or grimace. If these individual components are mixed up, e.g. an arm wave with a clenched fist is given by an obviously happy smiling person, then the final meaning is confusing.

After eating the leaves from several thistles both Bravado and

Macho moved on to follow the rest of the group. In a few minutes all was still and quiet again. I waited for a further fifteen minutes before daring to move. Then I carefully headed downhill to meet Nemeye, who had hidden himself well out of sight. I was still filled with a sense of wonder as we silently picked up our rucksacks and made our way down the ridge to find the trail back to camp. By virtually ignoring me, and carrying on with their normal daily activities, Group 4 had made all my previous hardships and frustrations worth enduring. I felt that I was at last beginning to reap my rewards.

CHAPTER FOUR

The elusive Group 8

In complete contrast to the peaceful intimacy of my contact with Group 4 was my first unnerving encounter with the five males of Group 8. When Dian first started her study there was an aged female, whom she named Coco, associated with the five males. One day Coco and Rafiki, the largest silverback, wandered off together and remained apart from the rest of the group – even sharing the same night nest on one occasion. A few days later Rafiki returned alone and Dian concluded that poor old Coco had died and had been left in the forest.

Never before had anyone recorded a gorilla group consisting only of five males. Dian therefore suggested that Group 8 might be a suitable research topic for my thesis. Unfortunately, however, they proved difficult to follow consistently because they seemed to travel both faster and further than any of the other study groups – perhaps because they did not have infants to look after. One day I was searching for them on the south-west slopes of Mt Visoke at an altitude of approximately 3400 metres. Eventually after five hours of toiling up and down ravines I found them just as a torrential storm began.

At last, however, the storm which had surrounded me completely was over. The thunder, which had resonated violently in the natural amphitheatre formed by the surrounding volcanoes, became a mere rumbling. I shivered, more with relief than from sitting still so long in the cold. In the aftermath the forest was eerily quiet and I felt even more cut off from the world below where, just two hours' walk away, people were working in their fields at the foot of the volcano.

Suddenly a bird began to sing, tentatively at first as though testing the world around it, then another joined in and the two sang a duet. It was a haunting song, especially beautiful in this remote mountain setting. However, it soon became part of a general murmur as the whole forest gradually came back to life.

I left the huge *Hagenia* tree which had sheltered me, and slowly followed the track as it wound uphill. I soon passed the spot where, one hour previously, just before the storm had started, I had glimpsed a shadowy figure. I pressed on upwards. After another ten minutes of creeping forward at a snail's pace, with frequent stops to listen, I heard some faint crunching sounds coming from over a small rise in the ridge just ahead. I crawled forward with my stomach pressed to the ground. When I reached the ridge and its cover of vegetation I slowly inched myself up to look ahead. At first I saw only the vegetation immediately in front of me. I lifted my head higher in order to look over the dense ground cover. My teeth were clenched so tightly that my jaw muscles ached.

A sudden explosive roar tore through the forest, and the birds stopped singing. The roar was accompanied by several piercing screams which made me open my tightly clenched teeth and rapidly catch my breath. Still roaring, a huge male gorilla accompanied by several younger males was charging downhill straight towards me. Now that I had been detected I stood my ground, for previous scientific workers had *insisted* that such charges are mere bluff, the animal stopping when he sees that you are not running away. 'Only if you turn and run are you likely to be attacked,' I had been told, 'but even then you are not likely to be mauled, for they just take one bite and let you go!'

But my confidence wilted as I realized that an animal of such an enormous size, coming downhill at such a speed, could not possibly stop before it reached me. Uttering a desperate, half garbled 'Who . . . oa!' I turned and leapt sideways to reach the shelter of a nearby *Hagenia* tree. I crouched under its inclined trunk fearing the inevitable, but to my amazement the gorilla did *not* appear at the spot where I had just been standing, and the forest was once more uncannily quiet.

I sat there, huddled up as small as possible, wishing that a door would open in the tree trunk and let me escape from this nightmare. As the reality of my situation dawned upon me I began to wonder whether I had been wise in choosing to study mountain gorillas rather than sticklebacks, snails or seagulls.

'Where on earth can he be?' I wondered. I turned slowly to my left and tried to peer around the tree trunk, but I could see only the surrounding vegetation. Suddenly a piercing scream from behind me answered my question as the gorilla discovered where *I* was. Without thinking, I leapt out from under the tree and ran off down the slope as fast as I could go, although I knew that one should *never* run from a gorilla charge. Scientific logic, however, now gave way to blind panic as I fled through the vegetation, my camera swinging wildly. But after only ten paces my foot caught against a tangle of lobelia stems and I fell face down among them.

'Now comes the crunch,' I thought, and visions of the natives who had been bitten while running from charging gorillas flashed through my mind. Unlike them I would not mind being ostracized for being a coward, but I certainly did not relish the thought of a large piece being removed from my backside! I looked up expecting to see the big silverback male bearing down upon me, but instead I was just in time to see him duck behind the tree from which I had just fled.

I suddenly realized what had happened when he charged. As I had jumped sideways, the leading silverback male, who was only two or three yards away, must have veered slightly and then stopped near the base of the tree. While I was looking round one side of the tree he must have been creeping round the other side, and, on seeing my feet sticking out, had screamed loudly in surprise.

I thanked my good luck and slowly moved to place my posterior in a less vulnerable position. As I did so I froze once more, for one of the younger, but still very large, blackbacked males was walking up the inclined trunk of the same tree. I recalled that the thing to do in such a situation was to pretend to be perfectly at ease, nonchalantly scratch oneself, feed from the nearby vegetation, or pretend to be a young gorilla and make gentle 'baby-like' vocalizations, as though one had a perfect right to be there and did this sort of thing every day.

Desperately trying to appear normal and casual I tried a

combination of all these techniques, while watching the gorilla out of the corner of my eye. He climbed up higher, walked out on to a large horizontal branch and stood there on all fours looking down at me. His position in the tree above me made him look even more impressive and I felt as though he was disdainfully looking down upon a vanquished enemy. As I lay there, cooing like a baby, 'casually' scratching my back with one hand and stuffing leaves into my mouth with the other, I suddenly imagined how amusing this would all appear to a fellow human had he been perched safely up another tree! I chuckled to myself and the tension broke. After watching my antics for a few more minutes the young male climbed quietly down the tree and with a feeling of relief mixed with disappointment I watched him follow the rest of the group, which had already moved on.

Despite the hours of toil that day I had few observations except those made during my brief but hair-raising contact. Somewhat dejectedly, I retraced my steps down the ridge-track. Nemeye's beaming smile showed how glad he was to see me safe and well for he had clearly heard everything. In his mind's eye he may have seen far more than I dared to think about, for he burst out, 'Those gorillas – they are *really* dangerous.' He well knew the males of Group 8 from many previous contacts with and without Dian. Laughing together in relief we picked up the bags and then ran like madmen down the ridge-track. By this time I was feeling much fitter and I enjoyed going down such paths as though running down a scree-slope. Young Nemeye was superbly fit and like two overgrown schoolboys we raced downwards. We soon reached the saddle area and once more turned left along the path which was now becoming as familiar to me as any road which one uses to reach one's daily place of work.

As we walked down through the nettles we suddenly heard the familiar tinkling of a bell, a sound almost as repugnant to us now as the bells of lepers must have been in biblical times. Since Dian had left I had already chased away many more cows and even raided the makeshift camps of the herders, destroying the temporary shelters which they made against large *Hagenia* trees, in order to discourage them from staying in the area. I even collected some of their spears and hand-made wooden milk containers, and this kind of retaliation seemed to have kept them away from the study area. But the bell we heard signified another invidious trespasser in the park. Nemeye stopped and listened. The bell rang again and this time was accompanied by a plaintive cry in Kinyarwanda. 'Poachers,' said Nemeye. Once more they were active along the trail we had used to drive the cattle into Zaire.

A bell is tied around the neck of one of the scruffy mongrel dogs which some of the poachers use. The tinkling keeps the poacher informed of the whereabouts of his dog as it follows the odour of bushbuck or duiker. When it eventually corners the quarry he is quickly on the scene to kill it with his spear or panga. Other poaching methods involve the use of pit-fall traps or wire snares, one of which had once almost caught around my ankle and I had narrowly avoided being swept off my feet and left hanging upside down. These poachers often leave their traps unvisited for several days or even a week or more. Thus any unfortunate animal which is caught soon after the trap is set dies a slow and agonizing death and then lies bloated, stinking and often partially decomposed until the poacher returns at his leisure. I hated this form of hunting. I therefore resolved to try and make the poachers as unwelcome as I had made the cattle grazers. My frustrated anger from the recent charge by Group 8 now had an outlet. I instructed Nemeye to try and pick up the poacher's trail and then follow it to his camp.

We quickly left the nettle area and crossed the westerly end of the meadow heading for Mt Karisimbi. Soon we reached a trail almost as wide and obviously as well used as a country road. Everywhere there were signs of cattle. Nemeye explained that this was a continuation of the trail we had used on our cattle drive and that in fact it was the main route used by cattle herders, poachers and smugglers since it ran across the border from Rwanda into Zaire. Such was their respect for a National Park! We searched around and Nemeye's sharp eyes soon spotted the tell-tale footprints, not of one poacher but of

two together with their dog. Nemeye decided that the tracks
were from the morning, made when they were setting out for
their hunting grounds. Since the majority of the local Hutu
population proudly wore plastic shoes whatever their state of
disrepair and wherever they went, it was fairly safe to assume
that these tracks of bare feet had been left by poachers, probably
pygmoid Batwa.

I had with me a small .22 pistol which Dian had left at the
camp. I took it out of my rucksack and we followed the trail
silently and carefully, stopping frequently to listen as we did
when trailing the gorillas. But our quarry were almost as well
fitted to the forest life as the gorillas themselves. Their incredibly keen hearing and eyesight, coupled with an uncanny
ability to melt into the forest and virtually disappear, made
them even more difficult to observe than my study animals.
However, we were in luck that day for these two were keeping
to the main trail. By following their tracks we hoped to be able
to sneak up on them rather than head directly for the sound of
the dog's bell and thereby possibly give away our presence. In
any case the sound of the bell had now ceased. It was near
nightfall and the poachers would be heading back to the camp
site they had prepared in the morning.

We travelled on, silent as ghosts, both determined to find
them before nightfall. Nemeye had a rare attitude, for he
respected the private lives of animals in their wild state and
hated the poachers' intrusions into these forests. This was an
unusual sensitivity, for in some African languages the word animal is often synonymous with the word for meat. In Swahili, for
example, *nyama* is used to cover both meanings and only the
context indicates which is implied. To many people what are
animals indeed except so much meat literally on the hoof? I
later discussed this, and our efforts to conserve the gorillas and
the forest, with Nemeye in my laboured and limited Swahili. I
was sure that he was not just politely agreeing with me, his
employer in the absence of Dian, but that he realized that what
I was trying to explain to him, in my own inadequate way, was
true. One day all the Europeans would have to leave, even we

ourselves, and then the safety of this whole area would rest in the hands of the Rwandese government, who in turn would need intelligent and conscientious conservators and park wardens of the calibre of Nemeye. 'Is it all just too naïvely idealistic?' I often said to myself. But what was the alternative? Was the whole principle of a National Park to be scornfully ignored by honey gatherers, cattle grazers and poachers like those we were tracking today? The same nagging questions were going through my mind as we crept through the forest.

I touched Nemeye lightly on the shoulder and he stopped immediately. His sharp eyes could spot gorillas often only discernible by me through binoculars, but my hearing, which had always been extremely good, had become most acute after weeks in the quiet of the forest. I used to try and hear the gorillas before Nemeye could spot them, thus the competition kept me even more aware of my surroundings. Now I could hear voices faintly in the distance. Nemeye listened, then nodded. I took a compass bearing in case we lost the track and then we set off again, now even more cautiously. As we approached I realized how right Dian was about voices carrying for immense distances in the quiet of the forest. The poachers were making no attempts to keep their voices down, and as we got closer we heard roars of laughter. Not only did it sound as though there were far more than two poachers, it sounded as though they were having a party! We crept closer and closer and the sounds of many voices became almost deafening, a hideously obscene violation of the peace and quiet of the forest. Amidst more raucous peals of laughter we finally crept along the narrow channel of a dried-up river bed and paused leaning against its bank.

The poachers were over the other side just a few yards away. We waited and listened carefully, hardly daring to breathe. At last we had found the camp site and, from the sound of it, a very large hunting party of ten or more poachers. I tried to visualize the scene over the other side of the bank, trying to locate the positions of the poachers by their voices, for they seemed to be coming from two places. I signalled to Nemeye

59

that I was going to try to peep over the top of the bank and slowly inched my way up. I had hardly raised my head above the bank when I, too, was spotted by eyes long accustomed to detecting the slightest movement in the forest, or the faintest thing different from the usual pattern. A sharp warning cry rang out and the camp before me literally exploded with small brown bodies heading for the safety of the forest.

Screaming like soldiers leaping from their trenches, Nemeye and I jumped over the top of the bank and ran into the camp. I fired my pistol into the air, but the sound from such a tiny .22 sounded more like a toy pop-gun. I then fired low at the running brown legs but they quickly melted safely into the forest. Suddenly someone burst out from the shelter of a nearby *Hagenia*, his weapons in his hands, and ran after his fleeing companions. Determined to teach them an unforgettable lesson I took careful aim at the poacher's legs and fired. He stumbled and fell as the bullet nicked his right calf and I felt unashamedly pleased to have hit him. He was still clutching his bow and, to my horror, he grabbed one of his arrows and fitted it to the string. I had only one choice, for I would not have time to reach the safety of the tree he had just left and I certainly could not dodge his arrow. I ran straight at him and fortunately reached him before he could fully draw back the string. I grabbed the bow and the arrow and pulled them from him. He then seized his spear and I had to wrench this from him also. I brandished my pistol and told Nemeye to tell him that he must go and tell his companions that they must leave this forest now and never come back to poach here, otherwise next time they might get shot. As Nemeye translated these words, shouting vehemently so that even the fleeing poachers could hear, I noticed for the first time that the poacher I had wounded was quite an old man. Nevertheless, I told myself, they must be taught this lesson so that they would leave the forest and its animals in peace, and I watched silently as the old man limped after his companions.

We examined the camp and found that it was a really large one. I had seen fully twelve to fifteen poachers as they fled. We now set about ensuring that they would have nowhere to sleep comfortably if they returned that night. The situation of the camp was ideal and I could not help but admire their choice. The large *Hagenia* tree, like so many in the saddle area, had enormous branches growing almost horizontally from near the base of the main trunk. This particular specimen not only had several such branches, but the tree trunk itself had a large natural hollow. To complete such a perfect tent the poachers had merely stuck twigs in a circle around the base of the tree on the side where it leaned slightly and set them against the horizontal branches. The twigs were covered with leaves and two small entrances were made, from one of which some of the poachers had fled. The others had been gathered around a camp fire a few yards from the tree. I crawled inside one of the entrances under the tree and found a large area some five metres long and three metres wide. A small fire smouldered in the floor in the centre sending out clouds of smoke which made my eyes smart and sent me crawling back out gasping for breath.

It was now getting dark so Nemeye and I set about our task of collecting up the belongings left by the fleeing poachers and pulling apart the tree house. Part of a duiker was still cooking in the main camp fire. Other pieces were stuffed untidily into the skin which lay nearby. From the smell this poor animal had been dead in its snare for quite some time before it was collected by the poachers. We threw the meat far out into the tangled vegetation in the nearby forest and set about looking for weapons. We found a veritable armoury consisting of six bows, twenty arrows, five spears, two pangas. In addition there was a filthy cloth bag. Nemeye smelt it, laughed and gave it to me. 'Bangi,' he said. I could not understand what he meant and examined the contents. In it there were revolting-looking hard, green, sausage-shaped pieces of compacted plant remains. I later gave it to Alyette de Munck and she confirmed my suspicions – hashish! However, our most important find was a polythene bag containing fifty francs, some keys and a set of identity papers. To my surprise the poacher was from Gisenyi, over sixty kilometres away. Nemeye and I shouldered the weapons and headed back to camp in the dark. The day had indeed been a most eventful one and I had a lot to think about as we trudged home.

Now that I had found Group 8 I was determined to follow them daily in order to discover what they really did during their wanderings – in particular to find out whether or not they followed any of the other groups. Unfortunately fate was again unfair and further heavy rain during the night obliterated their tracks, and despite Nemeye's superb tracking skills we lost them. After spending several more days searching the area thoroughly I reluctantly concluded that they must have travelled even further afield.

So the following day I set off with Nemeye and we travelled westwards around the volcano along our regular track. Normally we would branch off at some point and head up the slopes of Mt Visoke to our right but that day we continued around the cone and soon I was in terrain completely new to me. Nemeye told me that this trail eventually circled the whole volcano, but we could not go that far since the westerly slopes were in Zaire and I did not have a permit to work in that area. As we travelled quietly along in single file Nemeye, who was leading, suddenly stopped and pointed ahead. It took a few seconds for me to spot what his sharp eyes had seen instantly – a slight movement some fifty metres ahead. We paused and knelt down to wait and watch. The vegetation ahead of us was fairly open, consisting mainly of large patches of giant nettles surrounding a few scattered *Hypericum* and *Hagenia* trees. Even elephants could be hidden at times, but today this seemed unlikely. However, it could easily be a buffalo, a bushbuck, or a duiker, or . . . gorillas. I scanned the vegetation with my binoculars trying to find a tiny chink in its dense cover. How frustrating it was to be so near to a wild animal and not know whether it was as large as a buffalo or as small as a duiker! This feeling of frustration over the difficulties of making observations in such dense vegetation was to accompany me daily throughout my studies. I would often wish that I could transform myself into a small bird and watch unobtrusively from higher up among the trees.

The animal ahead of us was now moving silently towards our trail. I focused my binoculars on a point where I thought it would emerge and waited, teeth clenched with excitement. Suddenly two enormous jet-black, hairy arms swung ponderously out into the open trail. They supported a huge torso and a black shiny head – it *was* a gorilla after all. He paused and looked carefully along the trail to his right and left, then slowly and majestically crossed the trail. I could then see from the silver-grey hairs in the small of his back that he was an adult male – probably about ten or eleven years old and fully mature. I doubt whether he saw us for we were by now lying almost flat on the ground behind a small log which was covered with *Galium* vines. If he did he took no notice but headed directly for a similar tree trunk some forty metres ahead of us and to the right of our trail. He climbed slowly on to the trunk, sat down, and equally slowly and deliberately he reached one enormous arm across his chest and scratched his shoulder. His huge hand was held stiffly with the fingers curved like a great hook. They played no independent part in the scratching motion as human fingers would and this made the gesture seem ponderous and somewhat fearsome as the whole arm pivoted from the shoulder joint alone. After three or four strokes the same huge hand reached downwards and the black, leathery fingers curled tightly around the stem of a nearby nettle plant. With a gentle tug, the gorilla slid his hand up towards the tip of the stem thereby stripping all the leaves from its upper portion. I shuddered as he nonchalantly popped the whole virulent bundle into his cavernous mouth before reaching out immediately for more. I could understand that these spiny needles, which could penetrate several layers of my clothes, might not affect those leathery fingers but how did that delicate pink tongue manage? I could only conclude that during their evolution in such vegetation the gorillas had lost their histamine reaction – which causes the blistering swellings in humans – and therefore nettle leaves were no more virulent to them than lettuce leaves.

Several handfuls of nettle leaves were followed by some strands of *Galium*. It was now a familiar sight to see how the gorillas coped with the masses of tiny hooks on this herbaceous vine. Using both hands this adult male expertly hauled in strand after strand from where it was entwined around the nettles. Then with a rapid pivoting movement of his left hand he carefully folded the spiky strands into a bundle by allowing the hooks to catch hold of each other. This done he bit a large mouthful, then a second, and as he popped the remainder in his mouth his right hand was reaching out and pulling in more. It was one continuous and efficient motion of collection, preparation and ingestion. Having cleared the area immediately around the tree stump he climbed down just as slowly and majestically as he had climbed up. Before he disappeared I studied him carefully, looking particularly at his eyes and the patterns on the bridge of his nose which, as Schaller had shown, was often the best way of distinguishing individual animals. I did not recognize him as one of the study animals but I was not yet familiar with the males of each group – perhaps he was from Group 8! I scanned the vegetation for other signs of movement, but in vain. We waited some ten minutes and allowed the male to move off up the slopes of Mt Visoke then we cautiously moved ahead and examined the trail signs. 'It is only one – by himself,' Nemeye said, after scouting around.

This then was yet another unexplained aspect of gorilla social behaviour – a lone adult male. Schaller had already reported sighting almost ten such animals in this region some eleven years earlier. He had noted that they were of different ages and could not all be old males who had been displaced by younger more virile rivals. He never recorded any sightings of lone females and since his lone males were sometimes seen to be peripheral to, and even to join gorilla groups, he concluded that the life style of these males reduced inbreeding. He also suggested that perhaps new gorilla groups were formed by such males who joined a family group then left after a few days accompanied by one or more females. However, he had no evidence to support this conjecture. Considering the difficulties which would be involved in collecting meaningful data on such behaviour it was hardly surprising. Here was an unanswered basic problem of gorilla social structure – but could it be answered? One would surely have to have several observers carefully monitoring the movements and composition of several groups as well as the movements of any lone males – or join a gorilla group oneself!

Satisfied that this was indeed a lone male I recorded my observations in my notebook and then we continued our journey westwards. Suddenly the trail, which until now had been so clear, ended abruptly and the way ahead was barred by masses of nettles. This was as far as anyone from the camp had travelled for several months and the jungle had quickly covered all traces of human passage. Nemeye went ahead and expertly set about cutting a new trail with his panga while I followed, trimming it a little wider. I tried to copy Nemeye's rapier-like strokes with my own panga but I always seemed to have to use more force than he did. I later discovered that the men kept their pangas razor sharp so that the minimum of effort was needed – essential if one has to survive a long day's trail-cutting. Eventually to my relief we left the nettle field and the trail broadened out and was obviously well used by buffalo and elephant. It was like walking along a wide track in a park in England, that is until we suddenly reached a deep ravine, 'Leopard Ravine,' indicated Nemeye.

Dian had named it Leopard Ravine and had shown it to me on the map so I could now locate myself accurately. The surrounding vegetation was so dense that I had not been able to take a compass bearing of either Mt Karisimbi or Mt Mikeno for some time and I was relieved to know where I was. The ravine was only some ten metres deep at this spot, but higher up Mt Visoke it plunged down well over fifty metres in some places and was easily a hundred metres wide. Higher still, like all the other ravines, it gradually became narrower, shallower and eventually merged into the cone of the volcano itself. Similarly the lower reaches of the ravine eventually melted imperceptibly into the saddle area. Moulded by geophysical forces some ten thousand years ago these ravines were deep radiating scars set around each volcanic cone. On Visoke they were extremely regular and in aerial photographs they looked rather like spokes in some giant wheel, but many on the nearby jagged peaks of Mikeno and Sabinio were more sinuous.

There was a clear and obviously well used animal trail leading up the east ridge of Leopard Ravine. Since I could pinpoint my route on the map I decided to follow this trail right up to the top of Visoke if necessary. However, if we found any recent gorilla tracks crossing it we would follow these for they could well be those of either Group 8 or 9. In my mind's eye I could visualize that the whole region was made up of a mosaic of invisibly demarcated areas each used by gorilla groups as home ranges. Schaller had suggested that unlike other animals, even their fellow apes, the gibbons, particular gorilla groups did not keep these areas as 'territories' for their exclusive use. While each family group appeared to confine its activities to a home range area, much of this was shared with other groups, so there was a great deal of overlapping of home ranges. However, I judged that we were now too far west to encounter either Group 4 or 5 whose home range areas lay on the eastern and southern slopes of Visoke.

The trail rose steeply. I thought that I was now physically fit, but after the gentle track which circled the base of the cone this was really strenuous. After a while I felt that I was an actor in a slow motion film as I laboriously lifted one foot up in front of the other. Nemeye politely kept up a gentle pace but I still had to have frequent stops. Looking back on this climb later I think that I must have been suffering from lack of altitude acclimatization due to a week-end I had spent in Gisenyi down at fifteen hundred metres, then suddenly back up to camp at three thousand metres and now even higher. Keeping up a steady rhythm I forced myself on fifty paces at a time, then a pause, then fifty paces more. We climbed like this for over an hour. There was not a sign of a gorilla trail less than a month or so old. We eventually reached the zone of giant senecio trees and paused to rest and have a snack, sheltered under their bunches of shiny, foot-long leathery leaves. It was strange to think that these were related to the little groundsel which is a common weed in European gardens. However, I was now becoming more used to the 'African scale' where almost all living things were bigger than their non-tropical counterparts. Some of these mature senecios were probably some two hundred years old, for they are extremely slow growing, and I wondered what changes had taken place in these volcanoes during their lifetime.

Revitalized by the rest and some hot tea from a flask, we set off uphill again and I now eagerly moved faster. The heat generated by one's body during climbing is quickly dissipated by the cold mountain air at these altitudes and this discourages any long rest periods, especially on dull, misty days. The vegetation changed as we climbed higher and higher, the familiar lobelias – *Lobelia gibberoa*, which were ubiquitous lower down the slopes – were replaced among the giant senecios by another lobelia, *Lobelia wollastonii*. Unlike the thin rope-like stems of the lower altitude species the stems of *Lobelia wollastonii* became fatter and fatter as they grew until just below the spherical terminal leaf cluster they were almost as thick as a man's thigh. These stems were hollow and I found that the gorillas split them open and carefully scraped out the white inner pith with their incisor teeth. I once found one such specimen split into forty-three strips each bearing the teeth marks of a patient gorilla. However, there were no recent signs of feeding near this trail so we continued up and up towards the summit.

The giant senecios became more and more frequent, especially down in the ravine to our left, and the lobelias less so as we climbed. Suddenly the vegetation changed yet again as we reached the ericaceous zone of giant tree heaths. Some were rather like dense, overgrown heather clumps but others which were more scattered were distinct bulbous trees reaching four or five metres in height. As we climbed higher the ridge became even more open and our boots scraped off the thin veneer of moss covering the bare volcanic rock. To our right there was a wide expanse covered only by mosses, completely saturated with water which oozed out at the slightest touch. I scanned the open slope with my binoculars and noticed one large strip which was completely bare. It looked as though even the moss had failed to keep a grip on this steep wet slope where the water run-off must be considerable during heavy rain. Where the slopes were less steep I could see expanses of the silver-grey foliage of the alpine plant *Alchemilla cinerea*. We walked on and soon we were ankle deep in its soft, carpet-like cover. To our left Leopard Ravine ended abruptly with the dense green foliage of senecios and tree heaths giving way to a short steep patch of bare, grey pumice-like rock leading up to the open slopes on which we now stood. All around I could see more ravines merging with the slopes of the cone and with a feeling of excitement and achievement we hurried on towards the summit.

Although I knew what to expect, for I had seen it in aerial photographs, I was not really prepared for the amazing sight before my eyes. We stood on the brink of an almost perfect conical bowl which had two small peaks – one to the south-east and another slightly higher to the north-west. This latter was therefore the true summit of Visoke (3711 metres). The crater was awesome and impressive, for the inner walls curved steeply downwards to meet the jet-black waters of a crater lake situated some sixty metres below and stretching over a hundred metres wide. On some parts of the inner slopes of the cone were dense, monotypic stands of giant senecios, their gnarled branches adding to the unworldly atmosphere. Although Visoke was long since extinct my mind boggled at what lay in and beneath these jet-black waters. I longed to go down into the crater to examine it closely and scanned the slopes for a route down. Just then patches of mist came swirling around and I realized that it could be dangerous to explore further. We satisfied ourselves with a walk right round the crater rim, marvelling at the steep drop on the outer south-eastern side where some fault had left a huge deep bowl almost as big as the crater itself. Mt Visoke had apparently been first climbed in 1908 by the geologist Kirsch-stein. Others had since followed his footsteps and left their calling cards for I was disappointed to find discarded rusty tin cans in so beautiful a spot.

As we circled the crater rim we stopped periodically to listen for sounds of gorillas in the forests on the outer slopes below us. All was quiet and apparently desolate, but scattered droppings around the rim showed that most of the forest animals climbed to these heights – even gorillas, and perhaps most surprising of all, elephants. The sky darkened and the mist became thicker so I decided to return to camp. I was rather disappointed not to be able to see the other volcanoes from the top of Visoke but on reflection considered myself lucky at least to see the crater lake. In the 1930s Snowden, the botanist, had circled the rim of Visoke like ourselves and had not even seen the 'reputed crater-lake' because of thick mist. Climbing right to the top of Visoke now gave us one obvious advantage for, with a minimum of movement around the cone, we could choose a descent path to bring us down to any point in the saddle area around the immense base of the cone. I later discovered that the gorilla groups sometimes employed similar tactics when they moved quickly from one open slope to another much further around the cone.

Our camp lay to the south-east so we headed directly down towards it, but first we had to pick our way through an expanse of large hummocks of *Carex* sedges half a metre in height which were scattered like molehills over a relatively flat area. The hollows around the base of each hummock were filled with *Sphagnum* mosses covering pools of water ready to soak unwary feet. I tried to travel from one dry hummock top to the next but frequently toppled over. Eventually I gave up and, like Nemeye, I trudged through the freezing, *Sphagnum*-covered hollows. Fortunately this swampy meadow disappeared when we reached the steeper slopes and we were able to make good speed down another ridge path. We again passed through the various vegetation zones but at about 3300 metres we came across a large area of young *Hagenia* saplings each less than ten metres high. This indeed was strange for we were far above the usual height that these trees grow; I then realized that these were the first *Hagenia* saplings that I had seen, for those in the saddle areas were all mature giants with trunks often several metres in diameter and over twenty metres high. I was not to see similar young *Hagenia* until I travelled to the Kahuzi region in Zaire a year later.

We made our descent in less than an hour whereas it had taken us well over two to climb up alongside Leopard Ravine.

As we reached camp a hissing and roaring noise in the forest indicated our good timing and good fortune, for just as I opened my cabin door the first huge rain drops battered down on to the tin roof. Kanyuraguana quickly appeared with hot water for me to wash in, and the revitalizing flask of *chai*. Soon I was sitting by a blazing fire writing up my notes of the day's events.

I spent a further week searching in vain for Group 8, during the course of which I combed the saddle area right over towards Mikeno. I also climbed right over the top of Visoke once again but found only Group 4, in the region of the big bowl below the crater. I was extremely disappointed to think that Group 8 was to remain an elusive enigma.

CHAPTER FIVE

Family life

In the following weeks poachers and cattle grazers avoided the study area as though it were haunted. The gorillas, too, seemed wary and kept their distance, thereby making observations in the dense undergrowth most difficult. However, such days were balanced by the occasional good sightings, which made it all seem worth while. In addition I had something else to look forward to – Margaret and our daughter, Fiona, would soon arrive in Africa.

Dian had managed to arrange for us to rent a bungalow in Gisenyi, which Margaret and Fiona could use if they found life at the camp too rough. I agreed with Dian's view, however, that once Margaret saw our beautiful new cabin, which I had now managed to equip and furnish more comfortably, she would not want to live in Gisenyi. Still, it was nice to know that she could have more luxurious accommodation in the much warmer climate on the shores of Lake Kivu if conditions at the camp proved too harsh for a four-month-old baby.

As it turned out Margaret had no such choice about where to live when she first arrived in Gisenyi. She had been unable to get a visa when in transit through Kigali, and so we had to drive there in order to visit the embassy. After obtaining her visa it was then too far, and too costly in time, to go all the way back to Gisenyi – and so Margaret, unfit as she was, had to climb up to camp after only a few days in Africa. Fiona was luckier – she travelled up in her carry-cot on Guamhogazi's head!

Fortunately Margaret adapts very quickly to change and soon made herself and Fiona very much at home in the cabin. It was so good to be a united family once more. I returned to my research with even more vigour and enthusiasm. Life at camp now followed a familiar routine. Like any other man I would have my breakfast and then, bidding goodbye to the family, would leave for work. However, unlike most men as I set off from camp I was usually accompanied by an entourage consisting of Cindy, the dog, Kima, the monkey, one of the men to act as tracker and another to return Cindy to camp when I felt she had had sufficient exercise. Kima rarely travelled more than fifty metres outside the camp area but Cindy would happily roam for miles. We had to be very careful that she did not get near the gorillas, for previous reports indicated that gorillas just do not like dogs. Since dogs are often used to hunt them this was quite understandable. If the weather was fine Margaret and Fiona would often accompany me as far as the edge of the large swampy meadow. I would carry Fiona in a papoose-type carrier on my back from which she could survey the strange world around her. Thus our life was simple, exciting and beautiful.

My contacts with the gorillas, especially Group 4, were yielding more and more data as the group accepted me as a harmless part of the scenery, and I was able to make regular contacts with them under varying conditions. One contact at this time was particularly memorable. The mountain slopes were enveloped in a white mist. This itself was common but that day, far from being dark and storm-like, the mist was bright and gave a rather unworldly white glow to the green forest. When we had located the gorillas I was able to inch myself forward along a fallen *Hypericum* tree until I was in a position to look across the hollow in which the group were resting. Again the vegetation, although mainly only four or five feet high, successfully obscured the group, though they were less than twenty metres away.

Suddenly the tiny black figure of an infant no more than one year old raced up the inclined trunk of another fallen *Hypericum* only fifteen metres from me. He was quickly followed by a second infant and then a third. The highest point on their log was a tangle of roots covered with masses of vines. When he reached this the leader stopped, turned and stretched his arms out towards his two followers, and opened his mouth in a grimace. The other two continued their upward charge and soon the three were locked in a hopeless tangle of arms, legs and bodies as they wrestled with each other. Each had its mouth open wide and I could hear a faint growling, but it was obvious that no serious bites were being given and these infants were indulging in that most important of all activities for young primates – play.

One of the three broke away and retreated down the sloping trunk to disappear into the dense mat of thistles, celery and lobelias. The other two continued their struggle until suddenly one of them went too far and fell off the end of the log down into the vegetation some two metres below. I shook with inward laughter as the victor peered over the brink to find out where his opponent had mysteriously disappeared to, for in doing so he doubled right over while keeping his legs straight, thereby sticking his bottom up into the air. This was a perfect target for the tiny gorilla battering-ram which propelled itself like a miniature tornado up the tree trunk to abruptly end the temporary reign of the King of the Castle, sending him in turn tumbling into the vegetation below! Or so both I and his assailant thought, but he was much too athletic or too clever to be caught out this way, for he swung back on to the end of the log almost immediately. He must have gripped some roots as he overbalanced and was now busy trying to reclaim his throne. The third claimant quickly reappeared and so the friendly dispute continued for over fifteen minutes of uproarious fun before they finally ceased to climb back up after being displaced. It was one of the most naturally funny sights I had ever seen. I was to see more of this side of gorilla nature during my later studies and I never ceased to be amused by it, nor ceased to marvel at how like our own childhood play it was.

It soon became obvious why the infants had stopped playing – the group was on the move. Since they are carried by their mothers, for the first six months or so in the crook of her arm and then 'jockey-style' on her back for the next six to twelve months, and occasionally longer, the infants have lots of energy to expend while their elders rest. But once the group is on the move they must either climb quickly on to their mother's back or follow her closely so as not to be left behind.

I could hardly contain my excitement when I saw that once more the group was heading in my direction. Since this meant that they were again retracing their footsteps despite my presence this was a good sign that I had been accepted by the group. An adult female, 'Old Goat', was the first to appear. She reached the foot of a *Hypericum* only five metres away from me. I held my breath as she slowly and deliberately climbed up and then stood quadrupedally in the forked branches some two metres above the ground. She turned and stared questioningly at me. As usual I avoided staring directly at her but tried to watch her out of the corner of my eye.

Suddenly Uncle Bert pushed his way through the vegetation at the foot of the same tree. He stood there majestically, but only briefly, before continuing his travels. Two of the infants were still playing rough and tumble, for they wrestled and rolled past, apparently quite oblivious of my presence. Again, however, it was the young adults who came the closest. Bravado in particular lived up to the name that Dian had so aptly given her. She circled around the tree trunk on which I was perched and approached me from the rear. I slowly turned round to watch her out of the corner of my eye. Then I realized what she was interested in – my blue rucksack was lying on the ground at the other end of the log. She crept forward slowly and cautiously then, equally slowly and deliberately, reached forward with her right hand and touched my rucksack with the backs of her fingers. She then carefully put the backs of her fingers to her nose. Schaller had suggested that odour played little part in the daily lives of the gorillas but this act, and many similar ones later, was to convince me that their sense of smell is still important to them.

Having thus tested my rucksack, and presumably having decided something, Bravado stood there staring in my direction, though not directly into my eyes. As on the previous occasion Macho suddenly appeared. This time he approached Bravado in a play wrestle and to my surprise made a partial mounting – the first signs of sexual behaviour I had seen (and virtually the last!). Bravado rolled away and Macho followed. As usual the sounds of the group quickly faded into the forest. I marvelled that a dozen large animals could move so quietly, while I made as much noise as a buffalo.

The enveloping white mist had given an eerie, unworldly air to the whole proceedings. I sat there on the log looking around me at the strange vegetation – tall lobelias with their flower spikes sticking up like giant candles, surrounded by masses of thistles, celery, dock and bedstraw. Dead and fallen *Hypericums* lay scattered here and there in various stages of decay covered by rampant herbs and vines, and others still living raised their gnarled lichen-covered branches up into the mist. Their yellow, buttercup-like flowers contrasted sharply with the soft lighting and were the only bright patches of colour to be seen. I was exhilarated by such an experience and wished that Margaret could have been there to share it with me. I wondered what she had been doing down at camp on this magical day.

There were many days when the elements confined Margaret and Fiona indoors, days of heavy rain and hailstones. At such times they would need a bright log fire to keep warm. Then, while Fiona slept or played, Margaret would type my notes, experiencing some of the mystery and excitement of the work. At this altitude we were living with constantly changing weather conditions. Times of intense heat were unusual, and even then the air was often humid. One of the biggest problems of bringing the baby up to the cabin was that of getting her clothes dried and well aired. It often took a couple of days, and our cabin was draped each night with damp clothes so that the warmth from the embers of the fire would help to dry them out. There were days when the process of washing and drying the clothes got even more complicated. One cause was Kima, who delighted in dancing on the washing line with muddy feet so that the whole lot would have to be washed again. However, on one specific occasion she was not to blame.

Kanyuraguana was doing the washing down in the stream as usual when there was a sudden torrential downpour. Of course he rushed in to shelter, leaving the bowl of clothes on the bank. The storm lashed down for over two hours. When the rain stopped he went back to continue washing the clothes only to discover that the whole lot had been swept away. The stream had risen to three times its usual depth as it carried away the water from the upper slopes and the meadows and was now a raging torrent. Kanyuraguana was most embarrassed as he tried to explain what had happened. Margaret could not help chuckling to herself, but had to hide this and send him off to search for the lost washing. After half an hour or so he came back to say that he had found only one item. Still inwardly amused, she had to sound angry about his carelessness, since half the baby's nappies had been washed away. So the next day he had to search again. This time he was away for several hours and followed the stream as far as the shambas. He eventually returned with a bowlful of unrecognizable, grey and tattered items which he had managed to recover from the tangled debris along the banks. Margaret had to set about washing, boiling, bleaching and rinsing and finally mending them. After all that they were just about usable again and only one garment was lost.

This was the only major catastrophe on the domestic scene for the men worked hard to ensure that we had a constant supply of wood for the fire and hot water when needed. They kept the cabins clean and made repairs around camp, especially to the paths which often got very soft and muddy with the rain and needed masses of gravel from the stream to keep them in a usable condition. Kima and Cindy were well cared for, too. I think the men were quite fond of them, in spite of the occasional howls of protest which we would hear from the lower cabin when Kima stole something.

Typing and learning Swahili took up Margaret's mornings while Fiona was having her nap. Afternoons were times for playing with Fiona, outside when the weather permitted. If I was home we would all go for a walk through the meadows and sit for a while in the sun. All around was beautiful, soft green foliage with touches of pink from the wild orchids, weirdly shaped trees draped with mosses and lichen, and the majestic mountains in the background. It was wonderful to sit there quietly and listen to the birds and insects around us. We heard other sounds, too, the occasional bark of a bushbuck, once or twice the tinkling of a cowbell, and rather more ominously the calls of the poachers. Luckily this was always in the distance as they were still avoiding the study area and I never worried that any of them would come to the camp. The poachers, I imagined, would not want to complicate matters for themselves by troubling us there.

Night fell by 7.00 p.m. and Margaret tried to get the evening meal ready before it got too dark as she was worried about using a kerosene lamp in the confined space of the kitchen. Our most regular, and luckily favourite, meal was spaghetti Bolognese, as the local meat could only be tackled when minced. Our evenings were very cosy as we sat in the warmth of a glowing fire. We had much to discuss about the events of the day and we kept in touch with life outside through the radio and a weekly news magazine. There was reading and writing to be done, both of necessity and for pleasure, and our evenings were often interrupted by the little cheeky face that would suddenly pop up over the end of the carry-cot, pushing the mosquito net up into a hump. These were some of the most delightful moments for us as a family. An hour's wakefulness never seemed to disturb the rest of the night's sleep for Fiona, so we would indulge in getting her up at this time for a little play. After putting her back to sleep we would enjoy a cup of warm chocolate by the embers of the fire and then slip into our bed which had been warmed by several hot water bottles, a necessity as well as a luxury since the temperature dropped to below freezing point some nights.

There were no problems in this way of life for a young baby, especially as Margaret was feeding her herself. Later we managed to get sufficient cereals, bananas, eggs and milk to supplement her diet, and she kept very healthy. During this time Margaret was obviously committed to looking after Fiona first and foremost so did not get many chances to go out with me. However, there were several occasions when the gorillas were sufficiently near for her to go and see them. One day they were just behind camp and we reached their position by using a well-trodden elephant track. One animal, a young adult, was very close just across a gully and it stood and stared at us for a long while before gradually moving off through some lobelia stems and disappearing. We left then as all the group appeared to be moving off down into the next ravine into very dense vegetation. We were very disappointed to discover the next day that the whole group had later doubled back and crossed the path at the very spot where we had been sitting on a fallen log. Some had obviously stepped right over the log itself. However, Margaret, too, found that days like this were compensated for by others with better sightings. In particular she was thrilled to see the gorilla mothers, and noted how gentle but firm they were with their offspring! Most of all she enjoyed watching the play behaviour, especially of infants, which seemed to reflect a happy family scene.

Our life in the forest continued to have its problems as we continued the battle against intruders. A herd of cows literally surrounded the camp one day and while firing among the trees in order to chase them away I accidentally wounded one of them. It must have been hidden behind some shrubbery and was badly wounded when I found it. Crestfallen at my stupidity and its misfortune, I listened as it gasped for breath in the thin mountain air.

Until this moment I had hated these cows for the destruction they wrought. Prized only in numbers as a reflection of wealth, occasionally giving blood for food, but rarely eaten, the status symbol of cattle has caused the ruination of much of Africa's good land. If allowed to continue their indiscriminate grazing even areas such as these remote forests could become barren wastes, ravished by the herder's panga, with the soil churned to mud by countless hooves. Then the rain would wash away the soil to choke up the valley streams, leaving bare desolation behind.

Fear shone forth out of the cow's eyes and I knew I would have to put it out of its misery. Reluctantly I placed the rifle to its forehead and I pulled the trigger. The cow shuddered and jerked its head sideways, staring at me through one large, blue-black eye. 'Who are you,' it might well have said, 'to come here and review this complex situation in so short a space of time?

Who are you to act as judge, jury *and* executioner?'

Mumbling to the men to chase away the rest of the herd I slowly returned to tell Margaret my tragic story. An air of gloom seemed to descend on the camp and even the men seemed to be affected. Although they cursed the cows in the park, and chased them away at our orders, I felt that they were really only doing this since it was their job. Like many Rwandese they still used cattle as 'bride price' – indeed Kanyuraguana was saving some of his pay to buy a cow himself. Thus such animals meant more to these people than I could begin to imagine.

The morning after this incident I had great cause for concern when I found that Margaret, who had got up at first light, was nowhere to be found. I shouted to the men, who told me that she had gone walking up the trail towards the meadow. Fiona was still fast asleep so I locked the cabin door and hurried along the trail following the fresh footprints. Suddenly, just behind a large *Hagenia* tree at the start of the meadow, Margaret's footprints ended abruptly. I frantically searched around but the meadow had been so trampled by the cows that my inexperienced eyes were unable to pick up any definite tracks. Although I could see no signs of a struggle my mind feared the worst: Margaret had been abducted by revengeful cattle herders! Reluctant even then to call out her name loudly through the forests I raced back to camp and called Nemeye to come and check the trail signs. In minutes we arrived breathlessly back at the *Hagenia* and I watched anxiously as Nemeye scouted around. He eventually picked up a faint trail which seemed to wander around then head off towards Mikeno. Just then, to our relief and astonishment, Margaret's voice rang out. 'Hello – what are you two looking for?' It transpired that she had been so moved by the beautiful clear morning that she had decided to go for a walk and take some photographs of Mt Mikeno from the meadow – to discover that it was capped by a remarkable cloud formation which looked like a stack of upside-down saucers placed carefully over its twin peaks. Relieved that my fears were unfounded we returned happily to have breakfast. But in future I asked Margaret to tell me or the men if she went for a walk, and if she wanted to go far from camp, to be accompanied by one of our men.

The supplies we had purchased in Kigali only lasted us a few weeks. In particular we ran short of items for the baby, since Margaret had been unable to get sufficient baby cereal. We therefore decided to go to Kisoro where we knew we could get ample supplies. I would then take Margaret and Fiona to Gisenyi where they could acclimatize themselves to a life more civilized than on the mountain. We travelled down on a Friday and bought our supplies which were finally loaded into the kombie just as darkness closed in. Since the border closed at nightfall we spent the night at the Traveller's Rest Hotel and travelled to Gisenyi the following morning. After spending Sunday introducing Margaret to some of Dian's friends in the town I left them with a leaky, beaten-up old Land-Rover for transport and travelled back to the solitude of camp.

Happily, three weeks later, when faced with the choice of staying in Gisenyi to enjoy sunshine, swimming and tea parties or to rejoin me on the mountain she elected to return to camp. There she was able to share my experiences and give me help and encouragement. After all, she had not come all the way to Africa to be forty miles away from me.

CHAPTER SIX

A slaughter of innocents

I decided to call and see the Conservator of the Parc des
Volcans as we passed through Ruhengeri on our way back to
camp. I wanted to make arrangements for him to visit Mt
Visoke with his guards and carry out patrols in the study area –
hopefully to catch some of the many poachers and cattle grazers
operating inside the park boundary. I was completely unprepared for the appalling news that he had to tell – six gorillas
had been killed in the volcanoes. He was rather vague about the
details, except that they were certainly 'our gorillas', i.e. from
our study area. I discovered that even though the killings had
taken place over one week earlier he had not personally been to
find out what had happened, nor had any of his guards. I was
amazed by his apparent lack of concern over the fate of the very
animals of which he was the guardian – he even seemed to find
the whole affair rather amusing. I thought to myself, 'Surely he,
as Conservator, cannot have the same attitude to *nyama*
(animals) as the other villagers?' I left feeling completely dis-
illusioned.

In the market at Ruhengeri I found Guamhogazi and discovered that he, too, had heard the news. He said he knew
where the dead gorillas were lying and agreed to take us there
immediately. I had spent the past hour trying to work out
which of our study groups were most likely to be attacked.
Group 5's home range certainly brought them nearest to the
shambas, but the nagging possibility that this was a reprisal by
the poachers or cattle herders kept on crowding my thoughts;
if this was so, then one of the other groups was more likely to
have been attacked. To my surprise, however, when we reached
the new junction in the road up Visoke, Guamhogazi told me
to keep straight on instead of taking the usual right turn. Since

this road headed more towards Karisimbi than Visoke I began
to hope that the dead gorillas were not our study animals after
all. As we drove on further and further westwards I could see
that we were heading away from our study area towards the
shambas near Cundura at the foothills of Mt Karisimbi.
Suddenly, as we rounded one of the many bends, Guamhogazi
shouted, 'It is here.'

Leaving Margaret with Fiona in the kombie I followed Guamhogazi, who was scurrying down the grassy slope below the
road. 'Here, Bwana,' he called out. 'Here, one is here.' I
hurried over to him and then recoiled at the appalling sight
before my eyes. The carcass of a young adult gorilla was lying
on its right side, its knees pulled up towards its stomach as
though contorted with pain. I took a closer look and was
nearly sick when I saw that its guts had been torn out. Putrefaction was in an advanced state and the smell was overpowering.
All the bones of its hands and feet had been gnawed to stumps
by dogs or hyenas. The eyelids were firmly closed and hair on
the skull had fallen out in patches. It was a pitiful and revolting
sight, and my heart went out to the poor animal. Not only had
it experienced a violent death but its corpse had been defiled
by scavengers. 'Another is over there,' murmured Guamhogazi
in my ear. His voice brought me back from my mental wanderings and numbly I turned and followed him back up the slope.

We found the remains of a second gorilla, obviously a large
silverback male, in a small gully some fifty yards above the
road. It was lying on its back with its arms and legs stretched
wide apart. Its huge jaw, jutting vertically upwards, appeared
even larger since the skin and flesh had disappeared from
around the mouth and the enormous teeth could clearly be
seen. Again the abdomen had been torn open and all the guts
removed. This carcass was in an even more advanced state of
putrefaction than the first. Maggots were abundant on patches
of exposed flesh and flies were busy crawling in and out of the
eye sockets and mouth as they laid further batches of eggs.

The remains of three other gorillas were in another hollow
over the side of a nearby ridge. Then I noticed that the four
bodies above the road were surrounded by more rocks than

were scattered over the rest of the slopes. In addition I now realized that there were many smaller stones. Closer examination of exposed skeletal areas confirmed my worst fears – the gorillas had been stoned to death.

The Conservator had told me that six gorillas had been killed, but after a thorough search we could only find the remains of five. Despite putrefaction and mauling by scavengers (one in particular had had almost all the lower half removed), they appeared to be of two mature silverback males, one young adult and two adult females (or possibly sub-adult, blackbacked males). I took photographs of each of the remains, some showing the precise state and location of each, others showing the general location of the massacre in relation to the shambas and the nearby park.

The gullies in which the gorillas had been killed were between the lower reaches of long ridges which descended from Mt Karisimbi. Much of the area was either under cultivation, mainly pyrethrum, or recently cleared for cultivation. Although it was several hundred metres below the level of the existing forest boundary it could clearly be seen that the area was inside the line of trees which marked the old boundary of the park. But why had the gorillas been so far outside the forest? Had they been raiding crops as the natives so frequently reported, or had they merely been visiting part of their home range during the normal course of their travels only to discover that it was now cleared? I obviously had to get first-hand details of the massacre and so set about finding some local people.

With Guamhogazi's help as interpreter I questioned some passers-by on the road and workers in the nearby fields. Each replied that he had no knowledge whatsoever of the incident and added either that he did not live in the area or was not around when it happened. It was quickly obvious that no one was willing to give me any information. I headed back to the kombie full of anger, bitterness and frustration. Margaret was examining the carcass of the young adult just below the road. She was almost in tears at the sight of the crumpled heap as she, too, imagined it as it must have been in life. 'Why, why, why?' I asked Guamhogazi. 'Was it for food?' He recoiled so violently at the suggestion that we were immediately convinced that the Wahutu, whose main diet is a vegetarian one, would not stoop so low as to eat gorilla meat. But why had it happened?

With this question in my mind we left the gruesome scene to make our way back to camp. It was now late and thunder clouds were darkening the sky. We retraced our route to the road junction then turned up the steep roadway leading to the base of Visoke's cone. The clouds now released their full force of rain making the incline even more difficult to negotiate. As if to add to our troubles and misery the accelerator cable suddenly broke. In the torrential rain I tried to fix it, but each time it broke again when under load on the muddy slopes. We had no other choice but to go back to Ruhengeri for repairs. As a consolation I thought that I might also be able to get some real information about the slaughter of the gorillas. I taped the cable together again and then gingerly drove back downhill using the minimum amount of throttle. It took over an hour to reach town.

There we received conflicting reports: 'A woman was attacked by the gorillas while she was working in the shambas' . . . 'No, it was a child who was bitten in his thigh while he was innocently herding some cattle – so the villagers stoned the gorillas.' We were assured by everyone that *six* gorillas had been involved – but of the sixth we could find no trace. It therefore seemed very likely that it had been a young animal and was captured alive, probably to be sold illegally. However, despite many hours of questioning we could obtain no conclusive evidence of this, nor of any injured person from the hospitals. Next day we drove back towards Mt Visoke feeling even more depressed.

But this was not to be the end of our bad news; while we were unloading our supplies the porters told us that they had seen eight gorillas that very morning at the edge of the shambas. Fearing another similar incident to that at Cundura I tried to explain to them not to approach the gorillas and not to run away if they suddenly surprised one among the shambas – but who could blame them for laughing uproariously in disbelief at the thought that the gorillas would leave them unharmed and calmly return to the forest? I insisted (though I was still not sure at that time) that gorillas did *not* eat their crops but were merely after the *Galium* which grew in carpets of super-abundance at the edges of the shambas.

The next day I returned to the shambas with Nemeye and we searched for the gorillas that had frightened our porters. However, we found only old trails which led back up the slopes of Visoke. I hoped that they would stay there, but I offered a *matabeeshi* (tip) to anyone who came to camp to tell me the next time the gorillas were near the shambas. I showed the pictures of Dian standing near Rafiki, the largest silverback in the area, and explained that she was completely unharmed after many such contacts. Filled with open disbelief despite such convincing proof, the locals clung to their mistrust of gorillas. No doubt they would have liked to have known our secrets of survival amongst these terrifying animals, for surely it must have been immensely powerful *dawa* (medicine). How could one explain that it was a result of mutual trust?

I had arranged to meet the Conservator and his men at Cundura the following day. This was the earliest he could manage to visit the area – almost two weeks after the incident. He had agreed to bring his men on to our camp after the Cundura investigations, spend the night at camp and make his patrols in our study area the next day. After collecting six large sacks from Dian's store I set off down the mountain with Nemeye and Ndebeshe.

We arrived at the carcasses to find that even more had been eaten by scavengers and safari ants, and the latter were still abundantly present. The Conservator and his men arrived soon afterwards and I showed them the evidence of the stoning. I asked him to find the headman of Cundura so that we could find out what had really happened, but he replied that this was not possible as he lived 'far away'. It was obvious that he was not really interested in finding out what had happened. Seething with anger I set about putting the gorilla remains into the sacks with the help of Nemeye and Ndebeshe. The Conservator and his men sat on nearby rocks, lazily watching us, and roaring with laughter at our antics when we were bitten by the safari ants. When we were finally finished and had the sacks loaded in the truck they expected a lift up to our parking place. Since we desperately needed them to make patrols in our study area I could not give vent to my true feelings. However, I told Nemeye and Ndebeshe to sit up in the front with me and put the Conservator and his men with the sacks in the back, hoping that we had not brushed off all the safari ants.

Leaving the kombie with its guard, I collected porters for the loads. When the Conservator's men realized that I was paying even more than the usual porter's fee they all clamoured for the job. Politely pointing out that they apparently had an aversion to gorillas and safari ants I gave Nemeye and Ndebeshe the option of earning an extra 150 francs each, which they readily accepted, and then chose three others from my regular porters. To placate the park guards somewhat I dutifully handed round plenty of *tombaco*.

Unfortunately, my troubles with the Conservator and his men were far from being over. On our journey up to camp we heard the calls of poachers and all promised to be well for the guards' patrol the next day. However, we had only been at the camp for some fifteen minutes when Kanyuraguana came to tell me that the guards were leaving! I ran down to the lower cabin to find out what was the cause of such a sudden and drastic reversal of events. It transpired that the food that I had obtained for them was not to their liking. I had given the men from camp extra money to buy more of the food which they normally bought each week and there seemed ample to cater for the extra dozen stomachs. Apparently it was not the quantity which was in question but the quality. I was told that beans and maize were the food of 'hill people' and not of 'town people'! And so in a mighty huff they left. I was stunned, for I could still hear the poachers making their evening calls only a mile or so from camp. Eventually as a peace offering I sent Nemeye hurrying after the Conservator with several packets of cigarettes for himself and the guards, together with the reassurance that I would get the correct food for their next visit.

The following day I sent Nemeye and Ndebeshe out to find Groups 4 and 5 with strict instructions to make a careful check of the number of night nests. I hoped to be able to tell from this if any members were missing. Meanwhile I performed the most gruesome and unpleasant task of my life – sorting out the gorilla carcasses. These gorillas could provide invaluable information to science by their skeletal structure. Much of the taxonomic classification of animals is done from skeletal remains and gorillas are no exception, the skull especially providing a veritable gold-mine of data.

The classification of gorillas has had a chequered history. Early classification systems recognized up to nine sub-species of the genus *Gorilla*. Some were classified on the basis of only one or two skulls which were obtained from various parts of the same geographical region. This even happened in the Virunga volcanoes, where skulls from nearby volcanoes were classified into different sub-species. This proliferation of new sub-species was halted by Coolidge in 1929. After measuring over two hundred skulls obtained from many of the areas inhabited by gorillas he concluded that they fell into only two main groups – Western (lowland) gorillas (*Gorilla gorilla gorilla*) and Eastern (mountain) gorillas (*Gorilla gorilla beringei*). (Schaller later showed that most of these 'mountain' gorillas actually inhabited areas of *lowland* forest in eastern Zaire.) However, a very recent investigation had been published by Colin Groves from Cambridge. He concluded that the gorillas fall into three natural groups rather than two and suggested that only the Virunga (and probably the Kahuzi gorillas) are true '*beringei*'. However, gorilla skulls from within one area vary widely, as do human skulls, thus the accuracy of the generalizations which can be made depends upon the size of the sample analysed. These unfortunate animals, therefore, could now make their last contribution to science by increasing the sample size available for this area.

Such specialized measurements were beyond my equipment and my personal skill so the skeletal remains would have to be sent to an expert. But first all excess skin and flesh had to be removed and I had no laboratory facilities for doing this, only nature's scavengers. I could have buried the remains in a shallow grave and left the cleansing task to the many maggots already present in the carcasses but they would have quickly been dug up by Cindy, Dian's dog, or any stray hyena. In addition I felt that if they were open to the harsh elements of the mountain climate they would be cleaned more quickly. I therefore sorted out those bones which were already cleaned, carefully placed these in sacks numbered for each carcass, then laid out the rest in an exposed part of the meadow. After dividing each numbered set of remains from one another by small logs I surrounded the whole area with narrow tree trunks and finally covered them with fine wire mesh nailed carefully into place. This took almost the whole day but my labours were well worth it since in subsequent months Cindy managed to break in only once and stole only a rib or two. The skeletons were later measured by the Smithsonian Institute in Washington.

Later in the afternoon Nemeye and Ndebeshe returned with the good news that the nest counts of both Groups 4 and 5 appeared normal. It seemed likely therefore that the gorillas that were killed at Cundura were not from one of our four study groups. Of the two remaining groups, 8 and 9, the former consisted of only five males so this could not be the group which had been killed, while the known home range of the latter was sufficiently far away from the scene of the incident to rule them out completely. Thus the possibility that this was a direct reprisal for my anti-poaching activities was slightly diminished, but was never entirely eliminated from my mind during the following months. I never did find out the true facts of this incident but Sandy Harcourt and Graham Groom, who went to do census work in the Virungas the following year, found fresh gorilla carcasses with fingers and male genitals removed. This strongly implicated 'black-magic'-type practices, which occasionally occurred in some hill districts. I now have no doubt that some gorillas have met their deaths for this reason. The immense strength of large silverback males must surely be potentially powerful medicine in the eyes of simple people.

I now had to put this whole unfortunate incident out of my mind and concentrate my efforts on establishing good relationships with the study gorillas and continue my research. One morning, however, we were once more confronted with these problems by the surprise visit of one of our porters. He had come to tell me that gorillas had been sighted near the shambas. I was just about to go out after Group 4 but this was an emergency so I set out with him and Ndebeshe to find this unknown group.

All my contacts with gorillas so far had been with the groups which Dian had habituated over several years of painstaking work. The prospect of meeting an unhabituated group was exciting and somewhat daunting. Recalling my hair-raising experience with the supposedly habituated group of five males, I wondered just what additional thrills or terrors this unknown group could provide. In less than an hour we came out of the forest to see the vast shambas of vegetables and pyrethrum flowers which had rapidly replaced the once extensive *Hagenia* forest. The old boundary of the park could still be seen several kilometres away as a thin dark line of the few trees which remained outside the new limits of the park.

Soon we were sighted by the villagers and the cheerful greeting 'Mraho!' rang out loud and clear across the fields. I was still rather puzzled that the gorillas came so close to the shambas, for Schaller had reported that they quickly disappeared into the forest at the sound of a human voice, yet here a loud continuous banter was kept up almost all day.

Our guide turned off the trail and led us to an irrigation ditch which had recently been cut to carry water down to the new shambas some thirty metres below. Here he pointed out the obvious tracks where gorillas had crossed the ditch. The tracks were from that very morning so I decided to cross the steep gully and circle round above them, hopefully to see the animals from a good vantage point. After travelling about two hundred metres around the other side of the gully I climbed a tree to try and spot any fresh tracks. As I climbed further up the tree the quiet of the forest was suddenly shattered by the loud alarm bark of an adult male gorilla less than twenty metres away. Immediately a chorus of laughter, hoots, and cries of sympathy and advice rang out from the Wahutu working in their shambas. They must have thought I was quite mad to be approaching such obviously 'ferocious' wild animals.

Although I had been able to locate the position from which the vocalization had been given I could not see any of the gorillas. They seemed to be among a dense stand of tangled shrubs and vines. I climbed down the tree and went through my usual routine attempting to inform the gorillas that, like themselves, I was a peaceful creature, interested only in feeding or play. I gave the 'Uh-uh-u?' questioning bark which is given frequently on contact by adult males. A few minutes later I followed this with an imitation of a gentle chest-beat by quietly slapping my gloved hands on my thigh, and finally some loud foraging and feeding noises as I grabbed hold of vegetation and pretended to eat it noisily. All in all I thought that I gave a fairly good imitation of a small gorilla group engaged in its normal daily activities!

The real gorillas were either not so easily fooled or just not interested in making social contact. For half an hour there was neither sight nor sound of them. I circled round them to try to get a better view from below but the vegetation proved to be even denser there than above. Then predictably the rain started. For over two hours it descended with such force and volume that I feared that the light volcanic soil on the steep slopes around us, already wet from previous downpours, would be washed away and cause a land slip. However, like some giant sponge, the forest soaked up even these tropical downpours without suffering too much damage. Finally the rain stopped and I decided to back-track along the gorilla trail which had crossed the irrigation ditch in order to try and find the gorillas' night nests. These would give me an indication of the numbers and composition of the group we had contacted. According to our guide he and his friends had seen eight animals.

We found their night nests less than a hundred metres from the ditch, but despite a thorough search we could only find four nests which had obviously been slept in and a smaller fifth nest which had not. Older infants sometimes make such nests near nightfall but then often desert them and return to the safety and comfort of their mother's nest nearby. From the sizes of the nests and the lobes of dung in each, the group appeared to consist of one adult silverback male, two juveniles or young adults, and one other adult – probably a female with an infant, though no infant dung could be found.

I then returned to the irrigation ditch, following the trail left by one of the group. As I reached the ditch I was greeted by another loud alarm bark from the silverback and I saw the foliage move across the ravine. It was now almost 3 p.m. yet the group were obviously still in the same place in which I had found them over four hours earlier. I knew that gorillas did not move during heavy rain but sat huddled up without even bothering to take shelter, for I had seen it many times in the study groups. This unknown group had obviously decided that its extended rest period was over for they were now on the move. A 'Pok-a-pok-a-pok-a-pok' chest-beat rang out. It lacked the powerful hollow resonance of an adult male and, since it also lacked the slapping sound of the female's more flabby chest, I concluded that it was from a young adult. The foliage across the ravine moved slightly yet again and slowly the huge head of a silverback male appeared out of the dense undergrowth. He saw me and gave another loud alarm bark 'Waugh . . . h'! From the shambas down below the Wahutu added their own collection of imitation 'waughs' and other vocalizations.

I decided to try an experiment and see if I could make this group leave the area by pretending that I was a silverback male gorilla and that this was my part of the forest. I was not thoroughly convinced that Schaller's theory that the gorillas were not territorial in their behaviour was entirely true. I had already observed vocal interactions between the respective silverback leaders of Groups 4 and 5 when they detected each other's presence. Each silverback gave loud chest-beats, as they often did when they discovered my presence, but when meeting one another they preceded their chest-beats by an unusual series of hoots. These started as almost inaudible high-pitched panting sounds which rapidly ascended in volume and pitch then blurred together as the animal stood up momentarily to beat its chest. As they fell back on all fours the males would sometimes give the ground a mighty thump with their enormous hands. If not exactly determining a territorial boundary such vocalizations and displays certainly seemed to keep the groups apart.

Normally my imitations of gorilla vocalizations or chest-beats were very low-key affairs designed only to arouse curiosity or indicate peaceful intentions. Now I could really become aggressive against this paradox of the animal kingdom. Would he show the ferocious nature attributed to him by early explorers or would he remain the calm, peaceful creature I had come to know? I gave a long, loud hoot-series followed by the loudest imitation chest-beat that my leather gloves could ring out of the taut muscles of my thigh.

This had immediate and spectacular results. The silverback roared back at me in a loud, deep, threat bark. This he followed quickly with a chest-beat which made my puny effort sound like a baby clapping its hands. The sound rang through the forest and must have carried for over a mile. But I was not to be deterred so easily and roared back at him, following this with another hoot-series and thigh-beat, to which he replied with another thundering chest-beat. Perhaps he saw through my act and realized that I was an impostor, for he had not preceded a single chest-beat with a 'hoot-series'. I continued my bluff, adding another roar for good measure. He roared back at me even louder than before and illustrated well the power and resonance that his enormous frame gave to his vocalizations.

Our verbal battle obviously aroused the interest of the other gorillas for suddenly there were two more faces peering at me from the dense vegetation behind the silverback and these were joined by a third. One of them gave a 'Uh-u?' questioning bark – a sort of abbreviated 'Who are you?' I replied with a similar vocalization which seemed either to puzzle or satisfy them for a few minutes. Then the silverback did something to shatter the confidence which had enabled me to challenge and provoke him so violently, confidence which was based on the fact that a large deep ravine separated us. He now charged down the slope on his side of the ravine, which seemed to shrink visibly and become a mere ditch. My confidence was replaced by panic as I tried to think of how I could show him that really I was only bluffing, that this area was obviously his and that I would be quite happy to meekly go my own way and leave him in peace. Relief replaced panic as he stopped after a few more paces, but I looked around for a safe retreat just in case.

The other animals also moved out into the open. One was a large adult, possibly a blackbacked male, another was a young adult, while the third was a large juvenile. The large adult also came down the opposite slope a few paces and grabbed hold of the trunk of a *Vernonia* shrub. As though the three-inch stem was a blade of grass it casually pumped the whole shrub up and down a dozen times. This was the first time I had seen such a display from gorillas though many species of monkeys do this by jumping up and down on branches. It paused for a moment, then repeated the pumping action. At times its jaws opened and I could see the bright pink inside its mouth, but there were no vocalizations. Then it stopped shaking the *Vernonia* trunk, and sat down and began to feed on some *Galium* (bedstraw).

Meanwhile the silverback had retraced his steps back up the slope and was now standing quadrupedally, glaring across at me. His long arms and short legs enabled him to hold his body completely horizontal in relation to the steep slope. He snatched at some nearby leaves and ate them. Then he, too, sat down and began feeding on *Galium*. From this distance, some thirty metres, I could not make out the details of his face, especially his nose, but he seemed to be fairly old and had a very hairy appearance to his face with a slightly lighter patch in the centre of his forehead. The juvenile also started feeding and the scene now became a familiar one.

This, however, was not as I had planned. I wanted them to leave the area and go and feed elsewhere. A snapping sound from above the feeding animals made them, and me, look up. The young adult had climbed a tree and was looking across the ravine in my direction. The adult blackback moved up the slope and began to climb the vegetation growing around the base of the same tree and feed from a large patch of *Galium*. Then the silverback stood up, gave another chest-beat and this time as his arms dropped to the ground he stamped his right foot – an action which Schaller had also recorded. Was this in anger or sheer frustration? He stood there glaring at me across the ravine.

I decided to try my bluff once more, hoping that he would not decide to cross the ravine to settle the dispute but would concede gracefully and go on his way. Just as I was about to start, the wind literally appeared from nowhere and shook the trees even more violently than the gorilla had a few minutes earlier. I looked around and saw a dense mist rapidly approaching with an ominous black sky behind. The wind blew even stronger, and one of the gorillas gave an alarm bark, this time with quite a frightened note to it. The mist swirled around me and on down into the ravine, and the gorillas disappeared from view as large rain drops started to fall. In a moment the noise of the rain battering the trees was almost deafening. It was now half past three, and since this was likely to keep up until dark I retreated to the shelter of a *Hagenia*, put on my waterproofs, and set out to find Ndebeshe. Without a word we retraced our tracks to camp. My informant had long since retreated to the safety of the village, no doubt to spend his *matabeeshi*. I only hoped that he and his friends would understand my explanations. I later found that the unknown gorilla group did in fact leave the area and climb higher up the slopes of Visoke and were not seen again for several months – whether it was because of my 'territorial duel' I will never know. A more likely explanation was that it was part of the group's normal wanderings.

CHAPTER SEVEN

A chimp joins the camp

As the weeks went by I began to feel that my work was going
well, at least with Groups 4 and 5. Unfortunately, Group 8 still
remained elusive and I had managed to see them again only
briefly; they were still somewhat aggressive. Of Group 9 I
could find no trace, and concluded that they had gone right
round to the western slopes of Mt Visoke. Dense vegetation,
frequent heavy rain and mist still plagued my daily observations. Sometimes, however, the gorillas would come into areas
of good visibility, and then I would be busy scribbling down
notes about their behaviour.

Two days before Christmas we travelled down to Gisenyi, to
the luxury of hot baths, sunny beaches, and, best of all, to congenial company with other humans. In particular we had made
friends with the local doctor, Francis Dondeyne, and his
charming wife, Else. Francis was the most enthusiastic ornitho-
logist I have ever met, and he was extremely concerned about
the conservation of wildlife in general. He confessed that if he
had had the opportunity he would not have studied medicine
but zoology, and would willingly have exchanged places with
me. It was such a pleasure to talk to a kindred spirit and we
always enjoyed their company.

One afternoon Margaret and I were driving back from a
shopping expedition in Gisenyi. As we approached the round-
about near the beach road I saw a small crowd of Rwandese
gathered at the side of the road. They were obviously excited
about something and were shouting and laughing uproariously.
As we passed I looked to see what the commotion was all about.
I could hardly believe my eyes – the centre of their attention
was a young chimpanzee! I stopped the car immediately and
went to see what was happening.

'Do you want this chimpanzee?' one of the Rwandese asked as I approached. 'He is not expensive.' I was not really listening, for my attention was focused entirely upon the chimp. Someone, his captor presumably, had placed a wire noose around his neck and similar nooses around one wrist and an ankle. These had obviously been there for some time for the unfortunate chimp's wrist and ankle were marked by open festering wounds, made no doubt as he struggled to escape. The long, thick hair on the back of his neck appeared to have saved him from a similar scar in that tender region. The crowd were taking it in turns to pull on the wires and roared with laughter as the chimp screamed when the wire bit into his open wounds. Then they scattered as he tried to bite one of them. I was appalled by their complete insensitiveness to his obvious intense pain. 'He is only eight thousand francs, he is cheap.' This was about £80 sterling and more money than any of these men were likely to see in a year even if they had a job. I asked where the chimp had come from and was given the stock reply 'far away'. I tried to explain that these animals were protected and that they could not be sold in the streets. The chimp's owner looked at me in disbelief: the police station was only on the other side of the beach road yet the police had not interfered. He quickly explained that the chimp was not really his but belonged to a friend who also lived 'far away'. He was merely acting as an agent in selling the chimp; was I interested or not?

I certainly was interested in the chimp, but in ensuring its freedom from pain and captivity and not in paying him some outlandish sum of money so that he could go and capture more. I had already been sickened by the obvious market in Gisenyi for skins of many species of wild animals. These were sold openly by Rwandese in the streets or in shops by Belgian business people. None of them, African or European alike, seemed to consider, or care, that the market they had created spelt doom for many species via the poacher's snare, arrow or spear. Waistcoats, jackets, rugs and wall coverings were made from the skins of blue monkeys, black and white colobus monkeys and even from the extremely rare golden monkey as well as squirrel, zebra and antelope. The Belgian owner of the tannery had proudly shown me his workshop where dozens of Rwandese were busy preparing the skins of such wildlife, among them the rare golden cat. The owner explained that he was waiting for further skins in order to complete a rug from the golden cat hides. With obvious pride he had told me that frequently a large party of tourists would come over from nearby Goma in Zaire and buy up his entire stock. It then had to be replenished either from supplies in East Africa or locally, hence the steady trickle of traders that we had noticed coming and going, each carrying a bundle on his head. No doubt they, and the local workers, would be paid a mere pittance for their wares or labour while the finished products were sold for hundreds or thousands of dollars. Since the price paid at each stage depended upon the rarity of the skin, rugs made from the hides of golden monkeys or golden cats were the most expensive, and these animals were the most endangered. It was such obvious exploitation that I finally made myself unpopular by trying to point out to a mutual friend the threat to endangered species. I was pointedly told that it was none of my business.

Was the plight of this chimp any of my business? Did I really have any right to question the owner's attitude? I returned to the kombie to pour out my frustrations to Margaret. The crowd renewed its persecution of the chimp and we drove away with its screams in our ears, making us feel ashamed at deserting it in its hour of need. We went directly to see Francis Dondeyne and I explained what had happened. 'Do you want it?' Francis asked. 'If so we will go and take it.'

I had been so busy thinking about the poor animal's pain that I had not yet considered what positive action I could take if the chimp were suddenly my responsibility. Would it be possible to return it to a wild population? I told Francis that I thought that this would be so. There were none near our study area but one forest not far away was reputed to have chimps and no doubt this was where this infant had come from. Francis decided that he would go and see the chimp for himself so I drove him there. Since he was the town doctor everyone knew him and he was shown great respect by the crowd gathered around the chimp. He approached as though examining its wounds. Suddenly, he grabbed the startled animal, pushed it into my arms and herded me back towards the kombie while placing his own towering frame in the way of the irate owner who, now aware of what was going on, was desperately trying to reclaim his promise of wealth.

I jumped into the kombie, with Francis close behind me. Before he could close the door the owner had put his hand on it; Francis closed the door regardless, and the hand was quickly withdrawn. The crowd then gathered around the kombie and their mood was decidedly hostile. Francis wound down his window slightly and told the owner that it was illegal to capture chimpanzees and that I was one of the park authorities whose job it was to protect these animals. I was therefore confiscating this animal in the name of the law, and that he was lucky not to be arrested. This news startled the owner, who took a step backwards while keeping a wary eye on me. This was Francis's opportunity; we had left the engine running and he slipped quickly into gear and edged forward, scattering the gathered crowd. We drove off rapidly down the beach road. In case the crowd followed we avoided Francis's house and went directly to ours, which was further on.

The chimp had not taken his kidnapping too quietly. He was not able to understand our good intentions, remembering only the rough handling and the pain as the wires chafed his wounds. He showed his displeasure by biting me several times, drawing blood from both my hands. I quickly carried him into a back bedroom, laid him on the floor and retreated rapidly, closing the door behind me. Bathing my wounds with antiseptic, I contemplated our next move. The chimp had to be got out of Gisenyi and quickly. Unfortunately, it was now late afternoon and we could not possibly leave for camp until dawn the following day. I opened the bedroom door to go in and give him some food as a peace offering. As soon as he saw me he started to scream. Throwing the bananas on to the carpet, I beat a hasty retreat in case the noise gave away his whereabouts to the owner and his friends. Luckily the bananas, or my withdrawal, made him quiet once more. But what were we to do now? First I had to take Francis home and collect Margaret and Fiona before the chimp's owner appeared. This was soon done, then we were back in our house frantically packing behind barred doors, praying that we would remain undetected.

Luckily I had a spare pair of the stout leather gloves that were used to combat the mountain's nettles. I put these on and with the help of Margaret I managed to remove the wire from around the chimp's wrist, ankle and neck. Although he yelped in pain he made only one attempt to bite and I felt that he now realized we were trying to help him. I gave him further supplies of bananas to reinforce our good intentions and we left him with an old blanket for the night.

We were up before dawn giving a sleepy Fiona an early breakfast before packing her carry-cot into the front seat of the kombie. When we were ready I went to the bedroom to collect the chimp. He was nowhere to be seen! I examined the bars and shutters on the windows and to my relief these were still intact. A slight noise made me turn round and there, hiding under the wardrobe, was our *soko-mutu mtoto* (baby chimp). I tempted him out with a breakfast of bananas, then wrapping him in the blanket, carried him into the kombie. Margaret locked the front door and went to tell our surprised 'house boy' that we were going back to camp immediately and he was not to let any visitors near the house. We drove off at top speed along the main road out of Gisenyi, to bump on to the unmade road outside town with unusual relief. 'Mtoto', as he was quickly named, was curled up on my knee. I clutched him to me to try to comfort him, but he bit me several times as the car bumped along during the early part of the journey. Fortunately my gloves and extra sweater prevented him from drawing blood. Would he remain so wild or would he respond to kindness? Then what? Where could we let him go?

Fortunately, in order to get to the volcanoes we did not have to drive right into the centre of Ruhengeri. When we reached the crossroads at the edge of town we dared not even make our usual visit to the nearby post office to check our mail box. Instead we turned left and drove on towards Visoke without stopping. A further thirty minutes' drive and we reached our parking place and were immediately surrounded by the familiar faces of our porters.

They jabbered excitedly when they saw Mtoto. I held him close in case this reminded him of his recent frightening experiences. He now appeared to have accepted that I would not harm him and seemed content in my arms. He clung tightly to me, his long thin arms reaching around my body, pressing his tiny chest against mine. I could feel him breathing rapidly. However, I could not carry him up the trail to camp for if he became frightened he could easily escape, and the volcano forests were not a suitable habitat for a chimp. How was I going to manage to carry him? Suddenly I spotted the very thing, the ideal chimp transporter. It was a wicker basket one metre high and about half a metre in diameter. The Rwandese used them for transporting their vegetables to market. The owner rapidly parted with it for fifty francs and I set about getting it ready for Mtoto.

The basket would enable him to be carried like any of our other loads on a porter's head. Margaret lined the bottom of the basket with stout polythene in case he relieved himself all over his porter, then we packed some dry grasses over it, and finally prepared another polythene sheet to act as a cover for the mouth of the basket in case of rain. This complete we popped a surprised Mtoto inside with a bunch of bananas to keep him occupied. Tying the top cover on securely, I made sure that there was a strip of open basket-work sufficiently large enough to allow him to breath yet not too large in case it rained. A moment later and he was perched safely, and surprisingly quietly, on someone's head. Fiona was also lying quietly in her carry-cot perched on someone else's head.

In the meantime Guamhogazi had organized the remaining loads into line with an eager porter standing behind each. As usual he himself had picked the lightest load. 'Oh the perks of leadership,' I muttered to myself as I picked up my own even smaller rucksack! Poor Margaret still found the initial steep climb from our parking place the most gruelling part of the entire ascent to camp. It was still barely seven months since Fiona's birth so it was great credit to her determination and strength of character that she managed the climb at all. By early afternoon we were back at camp. After paying the porters we set about our urgent tasks – Margaret to feed our hungry daughter and I to prepare a home for our new 'son'.

Jutting out from Dian's cabin was a wire enclosure some four metres long by two metres high and two wide. It had been made as an outside play area for two infant gorillas which Dian had nursed back to health from death's door. They had been in the possession of the previous Park Conservator – though exactly how he came to have them was never discovered. It was intended that they should be sent to Cologne Zoo, presumably as a goodwill gesture to mark an official German state visit. Although she would obviously have preferred to have returned them to the wild, Dian offered to nurse the gorillas meanwhile.

They had long since left for Cologne and their play area had suffered the ravages of subsequent storms. Since the cabin was not mine I could hardly turn one of its rooms over for the chimp's use as Dian had done for the infant gorillas, so I decided to roof the outside play-pen area with corrugated-iron sheeting and line it with masses of dry moss taken from the huge pads which were abundant on the fallen branches and trees. I found a wooden box in our store-room which, when lined with more moss, made a fine sleeping box. For extra comfort I put in the blanket which we had brought from Gisenyi. After this was all prepared I placed an enormous pile of bananas, mountain papayas, blackberries and oranges in the centre of the cage and then went to show Mtoto his new home.

I jammed the mouth of the basket hard against the tiny doorway of the cage, then I cut the rope holding the polythene cover in place. Mtoto was out like a flash and tumbled down into the piles of moss. I quickly followed him, carefully closing the door behind me. I sat down near the pile of food and, picking a ripe papaya I held it out to Mtoto as a further gesture of goodwill. He was too excited to be out of the confines of the basket to be interested in food and set about exploring the cage, especially the new climbing bars I had just fitted.

After five minutes of exploration, including trying to open the cage door, he eventually came over to sniff the papaya. This was obviously to his liking for he immediately gave a series of short, sharp 'ugh-ugh-ugh-ugh' panting vocalizations, rather like those I had heard from the gorillas, but quite gentle. He grabbed the papaya and took a huge bite. Its succulent juices ran out over his hand and he vocalized excitedly again as he sucked them from the hairs on his hand. I had become so used to gorillas obtaining their water from their vegetarian diet that I had quite forgotten that Mtoto might be thirsty, especially since his main food in captivity seemed to have been bananas. This was obviously the case, for he quickly polished off four papayas in rapid succession followed by a handful of juicy, ripe blackberries. I could see that he and Kima would not see eye to eye over this rare delicacy for it took the men many hours to find sufficient for her alone.

Typically, Kima immediately appeared just when she was not wanted. With a crash, bang, thump on the corrugated roof of the cabin, then the cage, she was there hanging over the edge peering upside down at Mtoto and me. 'Ugh!' she called, and since her vocabulary seemed to be more or less limited to this sound, given in several different forms and with several different intonations, I was not sure whether she was pleased or annoyed to see our new addition to the camp. I need not have worried for in the following months she, Mtoto and Cindy got on very well and played together for hours on end. Typically Kima would tease Mtoto, as she so often did Cindy, then rush off up into the nearby trees if he became angry and tried to grab her. For safety's sake I had placed one of Cindy's old collars around his neck and made him a long lead of nylon rope. While this gave him plenty of scope to climb, Kima's cunning soon discovered that it limited Mtoto's movements and she would dance with apparent glee just out of his reach!

Mtoto's festering wounds responded well to treatment, though he usually quickly licked off any antiseptic I applied. However, free from the constant chafing of the wire, they began to heal. He soon adapted to life in camp and became as much a part of it as Kima, Cindy or ourselves. I had given careful instructions to the men that they were not to enter his cage, not even to feed him. They prepared his food, just as they did for Kima and Cindy, but I made sure that I gave it to him first thing each morning and then again early in the evening. I wanted him to have one person whom he felt he could trust and I felt that the association with food would be the quickest way. As soon as he began to trust me, and hence cease his fearsome biting, I began to groom and tickle him just as his own species would. This had an unforeseen consequence, for not only did he come to trust me but he also adopted me as his mother!

No one else could approach him, not even Margaret, and if he was ever in trouble with Kima or any of the men – usually for stealing food – he would rush into my arms and press his little body close to mine for comfort. Whenever I left him he would cry and eventually scream uncontrollably until I was out of sight. When he was outside his cage he soon discovered that he could keep a watch on our cabin by climbing the large *Hagenia* tree near the camp fire as high as his rope would allow. Like a tiny sentry he would sit there ready to vocalize and rush down the tree to greet me whenever I came out of our cabin or returned down the trail after a day in the forest.

I frequently took him for a walk when I set out in the morning to find the gorillas. All I had to do was to stoop down beside him and in a flash he would step from my calf and thigh on to my back, just as he must have done on his real mother's back. Unlike Fiona he did not need a papoose carrier, for his little legs were tucked tightly into the small of my back and his prehensile big toes gripped my waist. His long arms reached over my shoulders and his fingers were hooked firmly into my jacket.

Sometimes he liked to cling to my chest, so one morning I decided to carry Fiona in her carrier on my back and have Mtoto clinging on to my chest. It was a most satisfying feeling to be carrying two infant primates of different species, of one of which I was the father and of the other the adopted mother! It worked well for some ten minutes until suddenly out of the corner of my eye I saw Fiona's tiny hand reach out to poke Mtoto. Before I could stop him he had her finger in his mouth. I quickly pulled him away and fortunately his powerful teeth had not sunk in with their usual force – if they had Fiona would no doubt have lost a finger. Cursing my own stupidity I handed Mtoto to a reluctant tracker and examined the now screaming

Fiona. Luckily he had not even broken the skin, though he had obviously hurt and frightened her.

From then on we kept the two carefully apart for, like Kima, he became jealous of Fiona because of her relationship with me. If ever he saw me near her he would rush up and cling tightly to me, panting with excitement. We had only one further scare from him during the next three months and that was due to a misunderstanding. Normally when I took him out with me on my way to work, I would hand him over to one of the men well before we were in sight or sound of the gorillas, for I feared the possible consequences of their meeting together. He would then be reluctantly led on his rope, screaming for me, back to camp to be securely tethered to the large *Hagenia* tree by the camp fire near the lower cabin. Sometimes, however, he would be tied to the *Hypericum* tree just outside our cabin for he liked to hide himself in the large hole under its roots.

One morning, without realizing that Mtoto was in his hiding place, Margaret put Fiona outside our cabin door to escape the smoky atmosphere of the wood fire. She fastened her securely in her bouncing seat and went back into the cabin where she was making some tie and dye fabrics. Some time later she went outside to boil the hot water for the dyes. To her horror Mtoto was bending over Fiona and had his hands and teeth firmly round one tiny arm. Yelling for the men, and at Mtoto, Margaret grabbed the rope to pull the chimp away. As he was still hanging on to Fiona the poor baby was pulled along too, chair and all. Ndebeshe rushed up and managed to pull the baby away from Mtoto. Margaret led him away to the tree, quickly jumped out of the way in case he should turn round on her, and rushed back to see to Fiona. Luckily, again he had not broken the skin, but his teeth left a nasty bruise mark on Fiona's arm. We made sure in future that the two were kept apart – always. When I later read accounts of how adult chimps had actually attacked and bitten human infants to death, I shuddered at how short-sighted I had been.

By the time his wounds had healed completely Mtoto had become so habituated, and so attached to me, that it was obvious that he could not be returned to the wild, for he would probably approach the first human he saw and be captured once again. His future was a constant worry and I therefore wrote to Chester Zoo, where they already had an excellent chimp colony, to see if they would be willing to pay his fare to England if I could get the necessary export papers. The director wrote back to say that if it had been a female they would have accepted immediately, but they already had an excess of males. I therefore began making enquiries through other agencies to see if I could find him a good home.

Meanwhile I was busier than ever with the study groups. Early in January the cassette tape recorder which I had requested from Liverpool University finally arrived at camp. Now at last I could record more of the details of gorilla behaviour which were essential to a complete understanding of their life in the forest. My observations so far had been very opportunistic in that I made notes in a field notebook of whatever aspects of behaviour I felt were of importance. The obvious drawback of this method is that in order to write the observer has to look away from the animals and thereby may miss important behaviour patterns. By mounting the microphone in between the eyepieces of my binoculars I could observe and, by operating the remote-control switch with my thumb, record my observations continuously. This proved extremely satisfactory.

I had decided to concentrate my data collection on the feeding and ranging behaviour of the gorillas, i.e. what they ate and what they did not, where and when they fed, and how big an area they utilized for their feeding. Schaller had already examined some of these aspects, but I wanted to look into them in more detail. In particular I became interested in the factors which influenced the family groups during their everyday feeding and ranging behaviour. Why did they live and feed in groups at all rather than as individuals, like the duiker antelopes which were present in the same area? Or were the advantages of group life not to be found in their feeding behaviour at all but in aspects of their social behaviour such as mate selection or rearing their young? Were the daily movements of each group really as haphazard as they appeared to be or was there any pattern in the way they utilized their home range area? How were individual foods selected by the gorillas, and in particular how were infants able to choose the correct diet? As questions such as these began to form in my mind the outlines of my research strategy began to take shape.

I decided therefore to change my methods of field working completely. Rather than follow Dian's usual procedure of contacting whichever of the four study groups was nearest camp I decided to follow one group on a day to day basis and to record their feeding behaviour in relation to their movements. First I had to decide which of the four groups was best suited to this approach. Groups 8 and 9 were ruled out, 8 because it consisted only of males and was therefore not a 'typical' gorilla group, and 9 because much of its normal home range appeared to be too far from camp to make regular daily tracking possible. It therefore had to be either Group 4 or 5. I decided to spend one month's trial period with each to test both the suitability of the group and of the research project itself.

Since I had just spent almost all December with Group 4 I switched to Group 5. This was the only one of our four study groups which, in addition to containing animals of all ages and both sexes, had three adult silverback males, Beethoven, Bartok and Brahms. The latter was apparently frequently peripheral to the main group while Beethoven and Bartok were very much part of the group itself. Thus this seemed to be a well-balanced social unit to study. I therefore spent January following Group 5, and was quite surprised when I discovered just how far around the eastern slopes of Mt Visoke their range extended. I had some very productive contacts with them and my data began to accumulate at a most satisfying rate. However, I was appalled by some of the sights outside our immediate study area for poachers' snares were scattered liberally along the tracks and cattle were abundant almost everywhere.

One day when I was high up on Visoke I spotted a party of six poachers about three hundred metres below. Through my

binoculars I could see that each was carrying a bundle on his
head, neatly wrapped up in the skin of either a bushbuck or a
duiker. I knew that inside the bundle would be a carefully
prepared carcass ready to be sold from door to door in Ruhengeri. I raced down the trail after them but was too late to
catch such wily intruders. On the way back to camp Nemeye
and I discovered and destroyed two camps belonging to cattle
herders. They themselves were also too cunning to be caught
and I spotted them running away as we approached their
camps.

The presence of such obvious and frequent disturbances
could easily have affected the ranging behaviour of Group 5,
since the group clearly avoided any contact with such intruders. Therefore, near the end of January, I decided to switch
back to Group 4, which seemed to be less disturbed. My luck
was in and the group provided me with another truly memorable contact.

When I located them high up in the giant senecio zone they
were still busily engaged in their morning feed. Unfortunately
the vegetation was far too dense for me to get close enough to
see them clearly. To be able to do so I would literally have had
to get among the group itself – something which Uncle Bert
was obviously not prepared to permit! I therefore waited near
the edge of a clearing just inside a patch of shrubbery. Soon all
feeding noises ceased and it was apparent that the group were
taking their midday rest. A further thirty minutes of almost
complete silence confirmed this and I began to creep slowly
forward. I got within five metres before one of the group gave a
chest-beat. Uncle Bert immediately screamed out a loud threat
bark. I stopped, sat down and began to 'feed' on the nearby
vegetation.

For almost five minutes there was silence, then I began to
hear some very gentle growling noises, almost inaudible at first
then increasing both in frequency and intensity. The growling
was not an angry sound such as one hears from dogs, but more
gentle and good-natured. Occasionally one group member
would give a deep throat-clearing noise, 'Huh hmmmmm', and

others would take this up in a chorus. As these gentle vocalizations reached their peak I heard movements in the vegetation:
the group were coming towards me.

It was a most eerie feeling to be sitting in dense jungle
listening to the approach of over a dozen mountain gorillas,
and more so since I could not yet see any. Far from being full
of blood-curdling screams and crashing of vegetation – the
hallmark of Group 8 – this was a quietly electrifying experience.
I was again amazed that so many animals could travel with so
little noise. However, such tranquillity was suddenly rudely
shattered as Uncle Bert spotted me from only two metres away.
He roared a loud threat bark, stood up bipedally and beat a
rapid 'pok-a-pok-a-pok-a-pok' on his chest before falling down
on all fours and rushing away a few yards to the side of me.

I sat perfectly still and waited. All movements of the rest of
the group ceased for a few minutes then gradually began again.
Slowly the vegetation in front of me began to waver back and
forth. A tall thistle plant began to tremble, and it reminded me
of the many times I had seen a fishing float quiver in the water
when a fish starts to take the bait. Now, as then, I waited
expectantly. Again like a float the thistle wavered, then was
pulled down under the surrounding sea of vegetation. All
around me I could see the tops of other gorilla food plants
wavering, dancing and then mysteriously disappearing from
view, yet still I could not see a single animal.

Then the vegetation at the spot where Uncle Bert had been
was slowly parted and the large, shiny black face of an adult
blackbacked male, Digit, appeared. He paused, looked at me,
then quickly turned his head away as I looked at him. He sat
down about a metre away from me, where he remained for a
few minutes and casually looked around. His eyes focused on
one of my gloves, which was lying just in front of me, then
switched back to me. I immediately turned my head away,
though I was contorting my eyes to look back at him. 'Would
he dare touch it?' I asked myself, hardly daring to believe that
he would. For a further full minute, which seemed an eternity
to my squinting eyes, he slowly bent forward until his nose was
almost touching the black leather of the glove. I had prepared

my camera for just such a close contact and I gently squeezed the shutter release. In the silence of the forest the focal plane shutter fired like a rifle.

Digit immediately sat bolt upright and stared hard at me. I looked away again, scratched myself nonchalantly and gave a gentle throat-clearing vocalization. Just when I thought that I had frightened him too much he bent over again, and this time he picked up the glove. Giving another throat-clearing vocalization I quickly wound on and then pressed the shutter release again but this time he was not disturbed. He began to sniff and examine the glove closely and for one hilarious second I thought he was going to put it on. At that moment an inquisitive infant came up to see what he was doing. I took another picture under cover of another throat-clearing vocalization. Then Digit dropped the glove, got up and moved off without a sound. I picked up the glove, excited to think that it had just been held by him.

As though not to be outdone Bravado came even closer than Digit. First she approached me from behind then circled slowly round in front of me. She inched her way towards me walking quadrupedally. Then, when less than one metre away, by leaning her head forward and downward until she was almost toppling over, she sniffed my boots! I was desperately trying to turn my head away, watch her out of the corner of my eyes and get my camera focused at the same time, but judging from Digit's initial reaction dare I risk taking a picture while she was so close? As I debated she lifted her head back and moved off.

Surprisingly, she did not go right away but circled around behind me again. I had my back against a small *Hypericum* tree and I could feel rather than see her approach closer and closer until her nose almost touched my left shoulder. Then she reached up and climbed into the tree above me. Again I could sense her inquisitive nose approaching and this time she sniffed my hair! As though now satisfied with my body odour, she climbed higher up the *Hypericum*, accidentally showering me with dislodged bark and moss as she did so. Soon I could hear her feeding, no doubt on the tiny epiphytic ferns which grew abundantly on the lower surface of the branches. I sat there for fully ten minutes not daring to turn around and look up lest I frighten her. Eventually, amid another shower of bark, moss and dead twigs she quickly descended and made off after the rest of the group.

As Bravado went away I turned to try to spot the rest of the group. There, standing on a small hillock only five metres from me and completely in the open, stood Uncle Bert. The sideways quadrupedal stance of a fully adult silverback male is truly an impressive sight – Schaller had in fact suggested that this itself was a 'display'. I decided to be tactfully subservient and looked away from his gaze. After standing thus for another few minutes Uncle Bert turned and without a sound walked on up the open slope, then headed back into the vegetation.

The noise of the group soon faded and the forest was quiet once more. Suddenly in a brilliant flash of deep blue and red a turaco flew over the group. As it did so it gave its raucous chattering call, sounding somewhat like a magpie. The gorillas gave no vocalization whatsoever, presumably they were well habituated to turacos as part of the normal forest noises. Another noise in the *Hypericum* above my head made me look up – surely no one else was left up there? I scrutinized the tree carefully but could not see anything moving. I heard a noise again and spotted something scurrying along one of the upper branches. I focused my binoculars and there was a beautiful sun squirrel, his body about thirty centimetres long with a large bushy tail about as long again. He was busy eating the bright yellow flowers of the *Hypericum* tree. Finally he jumped from the tree to another and I was once again alone.

As if to mock such harmony a chorus of yelling and barking suddenly burst out from down in the saddle area. Poachers! I picked up my rucksack and went to find Nemeye. We would again try and deter this rape of the mountain sanctuary. Nemeye had moved off downhill when he had heard the gorillas approaching me. I met him at the lower edge of the open clearing. The noise from below was now almost deafening, dogs were barking furiously and men were shouting instructions back and forth across the forest – it was bedlam. 'They are catching a bushbuck,' Nemeye said. We started to run downhill, and as we did so we heard a loud trumpeting. 'Aye-aye-aye. It is an *elephant*!' Nemeye exclaimed in disbelief. We ran even faster but it still took us over twenty minutes to get down. By the time we reached the saddle area both elephant and poachers had gone, though we could still hear them in the distance.

We soon found the trail left by the frightened elephant as it was chased by the dogs. We followed as quickly as we could, stopping now and then to listen in case we could take a short cut. At one point there was a large amount of fresh blood spattered all over the ground vegetation, and from then on there were further patches on the trail as it wound its way downhill towards the shambas. My aching limbs and gasping lungs drew strength from some mysterious reserve and I ran on, stretching even Nemeye's mountain-running prowess.

After running for a further thirty minutes we suddenly burst out of the forest into the area recently cleared for the new shambas. We staggered downhill through the mounds of rich, freshly loosened volcanic soil, following the deep footprints left by the fleeing elephant. Ten minutes later we reached a crowd of Wahutu gathered by a narrow footpath at the foot of a small tree-covered hill. As we did so a great cry went up and I saw three men carrying pangas and spears running away as I approached. I raced down the path after them shouting and waving my tiny pistol, though of course not daring to fire. The watching crowd of Wahutu roared with laughter as the poachers split up and ran in three different directions. I followed one, but a lifetime of mountain living enabled him to outpace me easily and I was forced to let him go.

As soon as he realized I could not catch him he stopped and started to shout something at me in Kinyarwanda. I raced after him hoping that the slight start might enable me to catch up, but he was away in a flash, and again the crowd roared with laughter. I slowly climbed back up to rejoin them and was immediately confronted by several irate landowners demanding to know who was going to pay for the damage caused to their crops by the charging elephant. I pointed at the poachers, who were now standing at a safe distance from us. 'Those poachers, they will pay.' Realizing that I had seen through their act and was not going to give them compensation personally, the good-natured farmers roared with laughter, no doubt at the complete unlikelihood of my suggestion ever coming true. In fact little real damage had been done since there were as yet few crops planted.

I turned my attention to the now besieged elephant. It stood like a fortress on the hill among the only copse of trees for miles around. Freed from the persecution of the poachers' dogs, it now stood its ground waiting quietly, no doubt terrified by the ordeal of being chased from its refuge in the forest. I crept closer along a little path leading up the hill. A howl of warning went up from the farmers, 'It is very dangerous, Bwana.' After its recent experiences this would hardly be surprising, but I had to find out if it was seriously wounded. I paused for a few moments then crept forward again until I could focus my binoculars through a tiny gap among the trees surrounding the elephant. It was facing away from me but I could see a large gash in its left flank, no doubt caused by a spear. However, it did not appear to be bleeding much so I thought that it would survive. It was now late afternoon and I had to think of a way to make the elephant go back to the forest before dark or the poachers would return to finish it off. 'Dogs!' I thought. 'I'll use dogs just as they did.' I turned to retrace my steps. As I did so I dislodged a large stone, which rolled noisily down the path. My eyes flashed from stone to elephant as it turned its enormous head round at the noise. I could now see that it was not really a Goliath of an elephant but an immature male. With some relief I saw that it did not even have tusks. However, its large frame could still easily pound a mere human into the ground if it charged so I focused my attention on its ears.

Like gorillas, elephants charge at would-be attackers, but here the resemblance stops; for unlike gorillas, who have only one 'display charge' and therefore invariably stop before making contact, elephants have two types of charge, one being bluff and the other the real thing. I had read that one can tell which type of charge one is facing by watching the position of the elephant's ears: if they are held out sideways the charge is a bluff, but if they are held back flat to its head – watch out!

It was tossing its head, and its ears were flicking back and forth. I could not decide if it was debating whether or not to charge or just testing the air. It continued to shake its head, especially its trunk, as though it were in pain. Then I noticed blood on the end of its waving trunk, which appeared to be cut. Since it had not yet turned to face me I hoped that it had not yet realized that I was there, or had decided that I was no danger. As I focused my binoculars on the waving trunk, I could hardly believe my eyes – the end of its trunk had been hacked off, leaving a jagged mass of muscle covered in blood. Little wonder it was waving its trunk for it was no doubt in agony, for the tip of an elephant's trunk is well supplied with nerves, making it extremely sensitive.

Since an animal in such a state could be completely unpredictable, I tactfully withdrew as slowly and as cautiously as possible. I rejoined Nemeye and explained the state of the elephant to him. 'Yes, Bwana, they cut the trunk because now the elephant will not be able to collect his food. Now he will surely die.'

Whoever had had the nerve to get close enough to effect this gruesome amputation, no doubt with a sharp panga, would have many a tale to tell around the camp fire about his bravery – if he was still alive. However, such a feat did not alter the fact that this cruel deed had taken place *inside* a National Park – or had it? I suddenly recalled the awful tales I had heard of the European planter who had paid poachers to chase elephants out of the forest down into his plantation where he 'legitimately' shot them as marauders. He, of course, claimed the ivory as compensation for the damage to his property. Was this what had happened today, and was this any worse a crime than his? But this elephant did not have tusks so what was the prize? I concluded that it must be the meat, which no doubt could be sold just over the border in Zaire.

It now seemed hopeless to try to chase the elephant back to the forest, where if Nemeye was correct (and I now felt sure he was) it would soon die. I therefore paid one of the farmers to go down to Ruhengeri and tell the Conservator what had happened. I then paid two others to stand guard over the injured elephant until the Conservator and his men arrived. With little hope that either of these actions would save its life I sadly started on the long haul back up to camp. It was dark when we got back and Margaret was beginning to get worried. My wonderful contact with Group 4 was now overshadowed by the awful fate of the poor elephant.

The next day I went back down to see how the elephant had fared. It was dead. It lay on its side on the steep slope, its podgy feet sticking up in the air and its bloody trunk outstretched downhill. It had obviously either tried to feed or lick its wounds for there were patches of congealed blood all round its mouth. I examined the rest of the carcass, to discover that it had been disgustingly mutilated. As with the trunk the end of its penis had likewise been amputated and so had its tail. I looked at Nemeye and shrugged my shoulders in bewilderment. 'It is strong medicine,' he said, and went on to explain that the long, spiky hairs on an elephant's tail were braided together and made into bracelets which had magical powers and would keep away evil spells. I could hardly believe that even in this remote part of Africa such practices still took place – fortunately by a small minority of the people. However, I later saw such bracelets openly on sale in Nairobi, where they were bought as good-luck charms by tourists. Obviously ignorance and superstition are not the prerogative of any race or creed no matter how primitive or supposedly advanced.

I took some pictures to illustrate the elephant's fate then collected the kombie and drove down to Ruhengeri to fetch the Conservator. He was in a most affable mood and came back immediately with me to see for himself what had happened. I left him there collecting statements from the local people and returned to camp. Some weeks later I was summoned to make an official statement about the affair and I learned that they had caught two of the culprits. I was assured that they would be heavily fined. The Conservator's office was littered with bundles of spears, pangas, bows and arrows and snares of many types. He told me that each was to be used as evidence against poachers who had been caught at various times. I was impressed, and somewhat taken aback by such obvious diligence – had I misjudged him after all? I thanked him for his good work and told him that he could catch many more poachers if he would visit the camp again. He promised to speak to his men.

CHAPTER EIGHT

The bachelors of Group 8
meet the girls

I had received a letter from Dian asking me whether I would agree to having two American girls at camp whilst I was carrying out my research. She explained that they were intending to do some gorilla census work for her when she returned but that she would like them to travel to camp as soon as possible in order to get some experience of what the work entailed. Since it was vital to know just how many gorillas were actually left in the park I, of course, agreed and wrote back to say that they could come over whenever they were ready. When I looked in our post box in Ruhengeri one day I found a telegram from the girls to say that they were arriving the next day! I rushed back to camp, where Margaret and I packed ready to leave for Gisenyi at dawn the next morning. The two girls, Jacqueline Raine and Marshall Smith, eventually arrived six days later; they, too, had had trouble with visas!

Since I had told the men at camp that we would only be away for two or three days at the most, it was impossible to take Jackie and Marshall to Kisoro to buy their supplies. They therefore were obliged to obtain these from the more restricted choice in Gisenyi. We then drove back to Ruhengeri, where they bought milk and the rest of their supplies. Then they were keen to get started, though the climb to camp almost finished poor Marshall off completely. The combination of steep slopes and thin air made her literally gasp for breath. She resolved to give up smoking immediately, and such was her determination that she never again flagged behind.

During my absence the trackers had lost contact with both Groups 4 and 5, though Nemeye had recently found some fresh tracks further west than Group 4's usual range. I therefore decided to try and find them the next day. Since it had taken so long to get the groups habituated to my own presence after Dian left, I had no wish to ruin my work by suddenly confronting them with two new faces, so for the time being Jackie and Marshall had to be content with going out one at a time. Marshall was still rather exhausted after the climb so Jackie volunteered to be the first to go and see the gorillas.

We set out the following morning after breakfast. Marshall joined Margaret, Fiona, Cindy and Mtoto in accompanying us until we reached the large nettle field then they all turned back to camp, Mtoto as usual crying for his 'mother'. Marshall commented later on how incredibly upset he was when I left them, for they had almost had to drag him back to camp on his lead. Meanwhile Nemeye led us round the western side of Visoke and up the steep path to where he had found a gorilla trail from the previous day. We followed it to the nest site, where I showed Jackie how to find the nests, identify the approximate age class of its owner from the size of the dung, and finally how I mapped out each nest on graph paper so that later I would be able to see if there were any consistent patterns regarding the position of each group member.

Some theories of gorilla nesting behaviour had stated categorically that the leading silverback slept in the best position to defend his group; more recent suggestions were that the gorillas built their night nests in such a position as to receive the maximum amount of sun on them at dawn the next day! By mapping each nest site and giving each individual nest a score of 0–5 for various factors such as elaboration of nest, shelter provided, maximum amount of sunshine it could possibly receive, I hoped to be able to confirm or refute these suggestions. The evidence so far indicated a rather random pattern of nesting behaviour both with regard to any defensive position of the male and any orientation towards the morning sunrise, but more evidence was needed.

When the laborious task of checking each nest and measuring their relative positions on the steep, slippery slopes was at last over and I had made a plan of the nest site and recorded all other necessary data, we set off along the fresh trail left by the gorillas. After another two hours of travelling up and down ravines and crossing several slopes I suddenly indicated to Nemeye to stop. I tapped my nose significantly, for I had just got a faint whiff of the unmistakable odour of gorillas.

We waited quietly and listened for any sounds of movement. All was so peaceful that I began to think that perhaps the odour was not fresh after all but from the dung itself. I had made this mistake during my early days of tracking and thereby wasted much precious time listening for gorillas which were nowhere near. Just as I was about to tell Nemeye to carry on, a loud chest-beat followed by a deep-throated threat bark rang out from some fifty metres lower down in the nearby ravine. I turned excitedly to Jackie to nod in confirmation of her first contact with wild gorillas. She had gone white and was rooted to the spot. 'Don't worry,' I said reassuringly, 'that is just a mild alarm bark because they are not sure who or what is here. We will creep downhill slowly and quietly until we can see them.' Jackie went even whiter. 'Aren't we close enough?' she asked, trembling visibly. 'He sounds awfully angry.' I laughed, pointing out that as she well knew Dian had spent years with these gorillas and was unharmed and I, too, was now getting very close contacts in complete safety. Jackie was obviously not convinced, so I decided to sit down quietly and let her listen to the group until her confidence returned. We sat for over half an hour as they moved off down below us; judging by the sounds they were foraging and feeding as they travelled slowly along.

When the sounds were almost too faint to hear I signalled to Nemeye that we would go, not uphill as Jackie obviously hoped, but downhill to get some good observations. We crept down the trail for about one hundred metres before Nemeye's face suddenly beamed with delight; turning to Jackie and I he quietly indicated the other side of the ravine. There, slowly climbing up its western slopes, were no fewer than six gorillas. A moment later the silver back of an adult male came into view, followed almost immediately by two young adults. As I suspected from the location and the nest site count, it was not Group 4 but Group 9 led by Geronimo.

Jackie was obviously now much happier and more relaxed for the group were over the other side of the deep ravine, well over a hundred metres below us. However, we had good views of them through our binoculars so I did not try to get any closer. We were able to watch several of the group feeding on celery and thistles, and Jackie was excited to see a female carrying a young infant along on her shoulders. It was really a peaceful family scene and I was happy that she could now see for herself just how unaggressive these animals really were in their natural lives. We watched them for almost half an hour before they disappeared over the next ridge. I explained to Jackie that this meant the contact was now over for the day, since Dian never followed a group but always let it decide when it had had enough of the observer's presence. I jokingly suggested to Jackie that if she wanted to see more we could go to the top of the next ridge, but she assured me that she had had enough observations and excitement for her first day. I laughed and tried to convince her that these were our 'habituated' gorillas. Contacts with unhabituated gorillas, such as she and Marshall would meet during their census work, might seem more hair raising but they would be no more dangerous than these. Little did she or I know what was in store for us on our way back to camp!

We were well situated for making our return journey. There was no need to cut a new track or scout around for one we had previously used; we were already standing on a good trail and merely had to follow it down to the saddle area. In less than fifteen minutes we were heading along our main pathway through the nettle field. The cloud cover was dense and very low around the slopes making it seem much darker and later than mid-afternoon. We hurried on in case the rain started.

Nemeye, who was leading, suddenly stopped and gave his usual expression of surprise, 'Aye-aye-aye' and pointed to the trail ahead. There, cutting right across our main pathway to camp, were the unmistakable tracks of gorillas – and fresh ones, too. After examining them carefully, Nemeye reckoned they were only one hour old. 'This could be Group 8,' I thought, 'I've just got to find out.' I explained to Jackie that I had spent

weeks searching in vain for Group 8 and that this was a stroke
of real luck to find a fresh trail. It was important to know for
certain whether it was Group 8 and whether they were following
Group 9, or whether it was just Group 4 near the western edge
of its range. Unfortunately, Jackie knew a little about Group
8's reputation from Dian. 'Couldn't we leave it until tomorrow?'
she asked anxiously. I explained that such an opportunity had
never before occurred during almost six months of field work
and might never again. However, I suggested that if she was
too exhausted to start climbing back uphill then she could wait
there for us and we would rejoin her later.

Looking back, this really must have been a predicament for
her. For a young person fresh to Africa, to choose between
being left alone in mountain jungle inhabited by buffalo,
elephants and gorillas, or following the notorious Group 8, this
was a choice between the devil and the deep blue sea. I later
learned that some thoughtless Europeans in Nairobi had told
them the old tales, completely untrue, of gorillas carrying
women off into the forest and raping them! Jackie decided to
choose the devil and opted for Group 8. We turned uphill and
followed the fresh trail. All around was evidence of recent
gorilla feeding in the form of scattered peelings from wild
celery stems and their uprooted portions. We hurried on up the
slope.

Suddenly the whole forest above us seemed to erupt with
loud terrifying screams. We heard the pounding of heavy feet,
accompanied by the crashing and breaking of vegetation, bearing down on us. 'This can only be Group 8,' I thought. 'Stop!
Sit here,' I whispered to Nemeye while half pushing him down
behind a nearby *Hagenia* tree. When Group 8 were around
Nemeye needed no second bidding, and in a flash he was lying
face down beside a nearby tree.

I sat down at the other side of the tree and told Jackie to sit
close behind me. Just as we did so three gorillas hurtled through
the vegetation only ten metres above us. Two were fully mature
silverbacked males and the third was a blackbacked male. 'Is
this really it?' I thought. 'Is this where we get pounded into the
ground?' Would we now be the first to demonstrate that

The threat display of an adult male. In this impressive charge the gorilla came to within two metres of me. No real attack is ever made unless the intruder attempts to shoot or run away. (pp 15, 224)

A large infant was the first of its group to reach this banana tree. By the time the gorillas had finished feeding the tree was little more than a torn stem with just one or two leaves left attached. (p. 190)

(*Opposite*) A view of a ravine at about 3350m. from Mt. Visoke in the Virungas. I was following the trail of a feeding gorilla group; weeks later I tracked a band of poachers through similar country. (pp 33, 58–60)

This infant gorilla was playing with a twig while the rest of its group rested nearby. Occasionally it 'acted' towards me in an imitation of an adult's threat postures. (p. 186)

A silverback's 'bluff' charge at Adrien Deschryver in a bamboo forest. He reported that gorillas' behaviour is always more volatile in this sort of vegetation. (p. 224, 227)

(*Opposite above*) A blackback giving a chest beat. The pectoral muscles in an adult male are so large and taut that 'pockets' form beneath them: by striking with slightly cupped hands, these males produce a deeper, more resonant sound than other gorillas. (p. 49)

(*Opposite below*) Two young males, one almost silver-, one blackback, standing in open secondary forest. At the start of my study they would usually try to keep hidden, or partly so, behind vegetation. (p. 174–5)

(*Above*) A group's night nests, at dawn. Fresh nests are made each night and sometimes all the group sleep close together; the young usually sleep with their mothers. (pp 30, 90, 195)

(*Right*) Some members of a group resting in a bamboo forest. The lead male decides when and where the group will stop to rest or feed. (p. 48–9)

(*Overleaf*) Kelele, the leader of my main study group, keeping me under close observation. (p. 215)

gorillas were indeed ferocious beasts after all? But what a way to do so! I felt Jackie's head pressing hard against my back.

In complete defiance of my thoughts and the laws of motion all three stopped abruptly just as they came to the edge of the dense vegetation above us. I began to give 'pacifying vocalizations' as fast as I could, and nonchalantly looked around while scratching myself. Apart from the noises I was making there was now an eerie silence. Then the vegetation started to crackle as the gorillas crept slowly down towards us. It parted slowly in three different areas and three black faces peered inquisitively in our direction. Suddenly one of the silverbacks stood up and gave a loud chest-beat which sounded quite deafening at close range. As he fell back down on all fours he slapped the nearby foliage.

The blackback male, whom Dian had named Peanuts, shuffled right out of the vegetation and just stood there in the familiar quadrupedal stance. Although not yet fully mature he was very large and jet black. He avoided looking directly at me and was turning his head gently from side to side. Then he nibbled at some nearby stems but did not eat them. I noticed that they belonged to a plant which the gorillas did not normally eat. 'This must surely be "displacement feeding",' I thought. Many humans, when faced with a sudden perplexing situation, frequently do something completely unnecessary and out of context, such as scratch their head. Some animals appear to perform similar 'displacement activities' and often this takes the form of feeding.

Peanuts suddenly stopped nibbling the plant stems and stood up giving a loud chest-beat. Just as he finished he jumped up in the air with his short stubby legs, so that before his long arms reached the ground again he had been momentarily completely off the ground. The other two silverbacks, possibly 'Geezer' and 'Pugnacious', started to creep around to the right a few metres above us. Only moments later one of them screamed and charged through the vegetation just above our tree. He must have seen Nemeye and been surprised to find another intruder so close by. Peanuts immediately jerked his head to look in that direction then looked back at us.

He seemed very interested in trying to see what or who was behind me and kept sticking his head out sideways to try and peer around me. Then he moved forward and started to circle round to our left. I turned my head slowly to follow his movements. Soon his intentions were clear – he was going to circle around me and creep up behind Jackie. Out of the corner of my eye I could see the top of her head resting against my back. I then realized what could be making Peanuts so curious. Jackie had long, dark brown hair, not unlike Dian's, and this together with a familiar green bush-jacket, was all he could see. I recalled that just before Dian had left it was Peanuts who had crept right up to her to take a *Pygeum* fruit from her hand. Was Jackie in for a surprise? I had to warn her.

Peanuts was far too close for me to speak normally so I gave some more imitation throat-clearing noises together with some gentle, baby gorilla-like whines. He paused, then carried on circling around. I put the following drawn-out words into a whining vocalization: 'Do-o-nt moo-ove, eeven if he-e tou-uches you-u.' I felt Jackie's head bury itself deeper and deeper into my back. Peanuts was now out of sight behind me and Jackie later said that she could almost feel him behind her. Peanuts carried on circling round going past Nemeye without a sound, then quietly sat down less than three metres in front of me. He reached out with an enormous right hand and pulled down a nearby thistle plant, then with his left hand he daintily plucked off the brownish, immature flower heads and popped them into his mouth one after another. While still chewing he curled the fingers of his left hand completely round the stem of the same thistle plant about thirty centimetres from the top and in one easy movement slid his hand upwards, thereby breaking off the upper leaves and part of the tip of the stem. He put the spiky bundle to his mouth and took a large bite. Then he doubled the remaining long spiky leaves over and popped the lot casually into his mouth.

He then stood up quadrupedally and bit at the same sort of stem on which he had bitten earlier when displacement feeding. It split open and he nibbled at the pith, occasionally turning and looking at me. Again it appeared to be only displacement feeding. Then he stood up almost completely erect and jumped so that both feet were fifteen centimetres off the ground. While doing so he beat his chest rapidly about five or six times. As he fell forward his arms swung downward to support him. He was now less than two metres from me. He snatched at a yellow-flowered senecio plant and it swished past my face as he pulled it down. He did not attempt to touch it further but sat down staring intently at me. His right hand reached right across his chest and he began to scratch his left side, his enormous hooked fingers making a loud scraping sound. I, too, started scratching; he immediately stopped and stared at me, then when I stopped he continued.

He then reached towards me with his right hand, and I thought he was going to touch me. Instead he gripped a piece of the flaking bark on the *Hagenia* tree against which I was leaning and broke off a large piece. He sat down again, biting large chunks off the slab of bark until he had eaten everything. Then he stood up and once again reached forward to tear off another piece. This time he was unable to get his enormous fingers under a suitable piece to jerk it free. Undaunted, he leaned his huge head forward until it was less than a metre from mine and sank his powerful teeth into the bark. With a jerk he tore off a long strip which sent fragments shooting down all over me. He sat down once more and began to munch away at his second slab of bark. I slowly reached out and picking up one of the fragments of the bark I, too, began to eat. Peanuts paused and watched me intently, then he continued to eat his piece. He ate it all, but I could manage only one tiny mouthful of its tough leather-like texture.

I could hear the rest of the group moving slowly away. There was a strange horse-like neighing vocalization, but unfortunately I could not see who gave it or in what context. Peanuts remained seated for a further five minutes then he slowly got up and moved round the upper side of the *Hagenia* tree. Again he appeared to take no notice of the prostrate Nemeye, but fed quietly for a further twenty minutes before finally moving off to join the others.

Nemeye sat up giving a nervous 'Aye-aye-aye, whew-whew!'

which was plain in any language. Jackie, too, sat up and gasped with relief. 'Thank goodness they have gone!' she exclaimed. 'I am aching with cramp.' I myself had been so excited by such an incredible contact that I had not had time to think about cramp, but when I moved my legs I felt the shooting pains as blood once more began to circulate freely. I looked at my watch – it was just after 5 p.m. We had been sitting there for almost two hours.

'Did you see how close he came?' I asked Jackie excitedly. She shook her head and to my amazement she confessed that she had not seen a single thing! During the entire contact she had closed her eyes and pressed her face against my back. She had wished that she was anywhere else but where she was, especially when she could hear Peanuts getting closer and closer behind her. She said that he did not touch her, but she could sense his closeness and as she waited for him to touch her it became almost unbearable.

'Once they stopped after the first charge,' I explained, 'there was no danger – they were just curious. I am sure Peanuts thought you were Dian.' However, Jackie politely declined to share my trust in the nature of Group 8, and laughingly murmured, 'Never again.' Nemeye, too, was muttering 'They are *very* dangerous' and laughed in open disbelief at my explanations to the contrary. I played back some of the recording I had made of much of the contact and we roared with laughter at my high-pitched warning to Jackie. So did Margaret and Marshall when we played it back to them later, but they were in the safety of the cabin!

Undeterred by the recording and Jackie's comments, Marshall came out with me the next day to try and contact Group 8 once again. Now that I had found them it was important to make sure that they did not lose their 'friendly' nature and become unhabituated. Again they put up a terrifying charge display and once more they surrounded us. Unlike Jackie, Marshall had a superb view of them – her first sighting of free-living gorillas. I made some interesting observations on the way the 'round' of throat-clearing vocalizations, 'Ugh-ughmmm', travelled around the group, even joining in at the end of several myself. I tried to initiate other rounds but with only occasional success. In addition we saw Samson charge at Peanuts when the latter was approaching very close to us. Peanuts again sat and fed just in front of us, this time surprisingly on several dead, dry leaves, which he ate completely. Again they were with us for over one and a half hours but they were obviously extremely nervous and gave frequent chest-beats and charged through the nearby foliage. Samson in particular slapped at lobelia stems and one broke and fell right across my lap. When we got back safely to camp everyone was relieved to see us. I felt that Jackie was understandably envious now that Marshall had seen Group 8 – but she declined to take her turn the next day when I said that I was once more going after them!

This time they were resting in dense vegetation when we found them. It was impossible to get any closer so I decided to wait and try to entice them to come and see us. Marshall and I began to pretend to feed by crushing the nearby stems of wild celery and thistles. One minute of this and Group 8 were once more screaming and charging around us. When they had settled down I tried to get one of them to take a mountain papaya from my outstretched hand. Samson eventually came right up to sniff suspiciously at it but he did not take it. The group were more excitable than ever and actually came back twice after leaving us. Each time they gave more chest-beats, ground thumps and knocked much of the nearby vegetation over. Each time their charges brought them closer and closer. Finally, when they went off for a third time I decided to make a tactful withdrawal and we quietly slipped away.

During the following week I had three more contacts with Group 8. Jackie eventually managed to see them, though from a distance for they seemed now to be avoiding contact. I did not wish to press them just in case they did get too excited and accidentally charge into or run over us. This group, indeed, was an enigma and worthy of study in its own right, but both Jackie and Marshall politely declined the suggestion that they should make it *their* research topic!

During the next few weeks I took Jackie and Marshall to see the other study groups. We had some exciting yet peaceful contacts, with good views of animals which were far less aggressive than the bachelors of Group 8. The girls were also kind enough to look after Fiona occasionally, which enabled Margaret to join me while I was observing Group 5. One contact lasted for over three hours and provided us with some of our best views of infants playing together. These were friendly, bustling, domestic scenes and contrasted sharply with the cantankerous behaviour of the all-male group. They demonstrated clearly how different members of the same animal species can vary widely in their behaviour, just as humans do. Above all, these observations illustrated vividly that the gorillas were, indeed, mainly peaceful, sociable animals when undisturbed, and I felt privileged to have been able to share so much of their daily lives with them. I deeply wished that somehow I could communicate to them how I felt, for sadly we would soon be leaving.

Part Two

ZAIRE

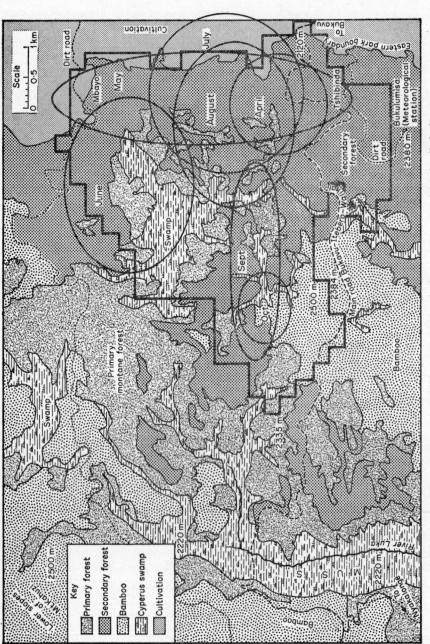

Vegetation map of my study area in Tshibinda (Kahuzi). The home range of Kelele's family is shown by
the heavy boxed outline. The ellipses show the group's centres of activity for various months.

CHAPTER NINE

Interlude in Kivu

In the middle of March 1971 Dian arrived back in camp and we left the following day for a six months visit to England. My relationship with Dian had unfortunately deteriorated during her absence because of misunderstandings which were made worse by poor communications. Our brief meeting on her return did little to improve the situation and several matters were left unresolved. We said our goodbyes to the camp staff, and gave them our warmest thanks for their cheerful help over the past seven and a half months. We had grown to like these happy people so much and were going to miss them on our return to 'civilization'. They gratefully accepted our gifts of excess shirts, socks and boots and told us to return soon. They had enjoyed having Margaret and particularly Fiona in camp, for above all the Rwandese love children.

We descended the familiar trail for the last time, loaded up our goods in the kombie, paid off our porters and after more goodbyes headed down the bumpy road to Ruhengeri. Half-way down we stopped to take a last look at Visoke. I was amazed by the differences which had taken place during even my brief stay. Pyrethrum now covered the area all around us and the shambas extended high up the nearby slopes.

In the distance we could see the plumes of smoke rising from fires scattered half-way up the cone of Mt Karisimbi itself, as the forest yielded to axe and flame. Disturbed, and worried for the future, not only of the gorillas and the park but of the whole of this region if the entire forest should disappear, we sadly turned away. We said our final goodbyes to our friends in Gisenyi, especially Francis and Else Dondeyne, and the next day we were on board the tiny aeroplane and flying over the patch-work-quilted Rwandese countryside. This, indeed, was the land of the thousand hills, and now for us a thousand memories.

At first it was good to be back in England. Our life of enforced solitude in the volcanoes had left us starved of social contacts with family and friends. It was most enjoyable to exchange news, discuss the events of the past year and just to see people again. But other aspects of being back were not so enjoyable. In the peace and quiet of the forest our senses, particularly of hearing and smell, had become more acute. This increased sensitivity, which had served me so well in detecting the gorillas in the forest, now made me hate English cities. I found the noise of the traffic deafening and the smell of the petrol and diesel fumes unbearable. In less than a fortnight I was longing for the healthy air and tranquillity of our mountain home. I now understood the intense pressures which, sometimes obvious and sometimes subtle, are part of the everyday life of urban man, making him more intolerant, more aggressive and more volatile than his rural counterpart.

However, I was fortunate to have this opportunity to visit England during my research. It enabled me not only to write a report on what I had already discovered about the behaviour and ecology of the gorillas during my initial field work, but to plan in detail the scope of the subsequent research for my doctorate thesis. This meant reading all the relevant literature, not only on gorillas themselves but on other primates and, indeed, on many other very different animals. One of the aims of behavioural studies is to make meaningful generalizations about the factors influencing the behaviour of all animals. Thus the findings of research on one species may give researchers working on other species ideas to examine or hypotheses to test in their own studies. This is especially true of studies concerning animals with similar life styles. One may first examine which factors influence the similarity in their life styles and, perhaps more important, those which make a particular species *different*, even from closely related ones. I therefore spent some six months in the Zoology Department at Liverpool University reading, writing and discussing the behaviour and ecology of animals with as many people as possible. I travelled down to Cambridge to talk with Professor Hinde and discuss the scope of my proposed research. I always found such meetings somewhat daunting but very inspiring, and I would return from Cambridge feeling like one of the disciples sent out to discover the 'truth' about animal behaviour.

The culmination of my return trip to England was to visit the Twelfth International Ethological Conference, which was held in early September at Edinburgh University. It was exciting just to be present at such an international gathering of so many students of behavioural research, to see and talk in person to many scientists who had previously only been names in scientific journals.

I met researchers who like myself were trying to find their feet in this relatively new field of science and were discovering more difficulties than answers. I also met experienced workers who had been through the mill themselves – some, indeed, like Niko Tinbergen and Konrad Lorenz, being the founding fathers of Ethology. The scope of the academic background was wide ranging, from neurophysiologists and zoologists to psychologists, anthropologists and sociologists. Thus the scientific papers and discussions ranged from the behaviour of single nerve cells in simple organisms to complex social behaviour in higher animals. Even the behaviour of man was discussed, from aspects of his aggression to the problems of autistic children. When the conference was over I felt more conversant with both my own particular line of research and how it fitted into the general scheme of behavioural research.

By now I had written my initial report and prepared details of my proposed field of research. I had decided to focus on one family group and examine the factors influencing its feeding and ranging behaviour. My equipment was ready and I was now eager to return to Africa. Unfortunately this was not to be easily accomplished, for during my stay in England it had become obvious that Dian no longer wished me to work from her camp; she had drawn up what she called a 'letter of agreement', and insisted that I had to sign it before I could return to work on Visoke. It put several obstacles in my way. Amongst other things, it stated that a research student's family would not be allowed to stay at camp. In particular it insisted that a student could not publish anything without first obtaining the permission of Dian herself. Since the regulations governing PhD students at Liverpool University would not allow such conditions, Professor Arthur Cain, my supervisor, suggested that I should abandon my project and find alternative research for my PhD.

However, I was reluctant to do this without first speaking personally to Dian to try to sort out any misunderstandings and explain my position to see if there was any basis for reconciling our differences. While I had made decisions at camp which had later proved not to be to her liking, I felt that I had made them in good faith. I felt that the projects I had now prepared could contribute something useful to her general research plan. Therefore I could not face merely shelving over a year's work and all the plans we had made to return to Visoke.

The final decision to go back was not taken lightly. Like myself, Margaret was loath to be beaten by circumstances, especially as we had already achieved so much, but she was anxious that I should not drive myself too far in trying to overcome the problems. Such conflict led to some very heated discussions and was a great strain on us both. In the end I persuaded both Margaret and Professor Cain that it would be best for me to return to Rwanda and discuss the whole situation with Dian. If then there was no hope of my continuing without signing the letter of agreement, I agreed to abandon my project and return home. I wrote again to Dian to explain the situation once more and to say that I was on my way to Rwanda – but first I was to visit Zaire to see some other mountain gorillas.

During my stay on Visoke I had written to Dr Peter Kunkel, who was then the Director General of IRSAC (Institut pour la Recherche Scientifique en Afrique Centrale), at Lwiro, Bukavu, on the subject of mountain gorillas. He had written back telling me that he was organizing a two-year programme of research on tropical forest ecology to start in 1971, and that gorillas were among the animals to be studied. He invited me to visit IRSAC to discuss matters of mutual interest with the scientists who would be commencing their research in the montane forests of the Kahuzi-Biega National Park. Since this also meant an opportunity to see gorillas in a geographical area other than the volcanoes I gladly accepted his invitation and wrote to say that I would be arriving at the end of September. When my flight was confirmed I sent a telegram to give details of my time of arrival. I still didn't know African communications, for both letter and telegram arrived only two hours before I did!

Fortunately for me Peter Kunkel was the sort of man who took such minor problems in his stride. When I disembarked from the Air Zaire flight, my mind still reeling from eight hours of non-stop Zairois music, he was at Kavumu airport to meet me. Of German nationality but widely travelled, he quickly spotted the 'puzzled-looking Englishman' amongst the crowd of Belgian and Zairois passengers and came to introduce himself. I liked him instantly from his firm, friendly handshake and the sincere sparkle in his piercing eyes. Little did I know then how much he was to help me and to influence my thinking about Africa.

With his help I quickly had my bags cleared through customs, for everyone seemed to know him personally. Soon we were in his Volkswagen and speeding up the straight tarmaced road towards the shanty town of Kavumu itself. At Kavumu the road joined the main Goma–Bukavu road. To our left it went south to Bukavu, the capital of the Kivu province, and was tarmaced all the way, while to our right it went north alongside the west bank of Lake Kivu to Goma and was un-tarmaced. We turned right and immediately I felt that I was really back in Africa, for the kombie stopped behaving like a smooth comfortable automobile and shook every bone in my body. I shall never forget the first ride with Peter (nor any other) for he drove faster than I would ever dare on such roads and, as was the local custom, he frequently changed sides depending upon which was the better surface.

After ten minutes of such hectic driving we turned left at an impressive Gothic-script sign indicating 'IRSAC'. A few more minutes brought us to a huge arched gateway with two pairs of gates. As we sped onwards the gateman rushed out of his little house and opened the gates. With a wave of thanks we

drove through and into the extensive grounds of IRSAC itself.
I was surprised to see that there was a football pitch until I
discovered how fanatical the Zairois are about football. We
drove on past several houses and pavilions, each with masses
of beautiful tropical flowers in their gardens. Passing a large
stone building, which I later discovered was the guest house,
we reached the main building of the institute itself. I had not
expected anything of this nature or scale. The buildings were
built around a rectangular courtyard about one hundred
metres long and fifty metres wide. Across the front ran an
impressive covered entrance-way, flanked by circular buttresses
containing rooms on either side. Behind the entrance-way were
two open pools filled with tropical water plants and from them
came the hum of insects and the occasional croaking calls of
tree frogs.

Dr Kunkel led me towards his office. We passed through a
large conference room, which contained the longest table I have
ever seen, fully seven metres long and surrounded by numerous
large, curved chairs. The dark wood panelling on the walls
gave the room a formal, rather austere atmosphere. Striding
past the long table he opened the enormous door leading into
his private office. It was circular, with two huge desks, one on
either side of the room. The same rich wood panelling covered
much of the walls but the bright light from several large
windows made this room much less austere than the others.
Dr Kunkel could see that I was amazed by my surroundings.
He told me to sit down while he explained how this impressive
building came to be here in central Africa.

IRSAC was started by a decree of the Belgian Prince Regent,
Charles, on 1 July 1947. It began first at Uvira (near Bujum-
bura), where a large, old hotel was transferred into a research
centre. Later it opened another centre at Astrida (now Butare).
Eventually the main centre in which we were now seated was
built in 1951 at Lwiro near Bukavu in the Kivu province of
Zaire. According to the decree the work of the institute was to
be scientific research concerned with man and nature. Ultim-
ately five research centres, each with permanent European
staff, were established. These were Uvira, which specialized

in hydrology; Astrida (Butare) for social anthropology; Elizabethville (Lubumbashi) for industrial medicine; Mabali for botany; and Lwiro, where studies in such diverse fields as human nutrition and parasitology, urology, zoology, botany and geophysics were undertaken. The four smaller centres were each permanently manned by five research fellows, while the main station here at Lwiro had some forty scientists and technicians of many nationalities. In addition many temporary field centres were opened for a year or so, but three became permanent stations. One was at Irangi in the dense equatorial rain forest near the Zaire basin, while the other two were in Rwanda – one in the Rugere forest and the other near the Kagera National Park.

After independence the stations in Rwanda remained under Belgian control while those in Zaire became national property. A few Belgians remained in each as technical assistants, but the decade of the sixties was a most turbulent one in this region and the upheavals in 1964 and 1967 caused all work virtually to cease for several years. However, the head of state, President Mobutu Sese Seko, who came into office in November 1965, eventually brought stability to this troubled country. IRSAC itself was placed under the direct responsibility of the 'Présidence de la République', and was thus assured of government support and finance.

Dr Kunkel himself had been working in the zoology section at IRSAC since May 1963. In December 1969 he became Director General; thus he and his family had been through both the peaceful and troubled eras in the institute's short history. Now, thanks to the welcome peace and calm, he was busily engaged in getting work resumed on as many scientific research programmes as possible. Work had long since started on some, and these, in true IRSAC tradition, were in diverse scientific fields, including geology; seismology; ethnographic studies of the peoples around Lake Kivu; the problems of combating malnutrition and, recently, a study of tropical rain forest ecology. This latter project was being financed by the Volkswagen Foundation and was to include ecological studies on the pygmies of the forest as well as on many animal and plant species, including the mountain gorilla. The research in the various projects was being carried out by a wide range of scientists and technicians of many nationalities: Zairois, Rwandese, Belgians, French, Germans, Americans, and recently Japanese. As I listened, thoroughly absorbed, it all sounded exciting, intellectually stimulating and very international in flavour.

I was then given a tour of the well-equipped research laboratories and the superb library. Dr Kunkel kindly offered the help of the institute's resources in any aspect of my own research. Rather overwhelmed, I then joined him once more in the kombie as we set out for his house at Tshibati. The climb up the winding, bumpy, unmade road provided some tantalizing glimpses of the surrounding countryside and, in places, of Lake Kivu itself. We travelled several kilometres over roads even worse than those down below before we reached our destination, a long, low, white painted villa with a courtyard at the rear. The front of the villa was reached via a wide archway separating a small annexe from the main building. As we passed through the archway the view that greeted me was breathtakingly beautiful. In the foreground stretched a large lawn which sloped gently downhill. Behind this were neat lines of banana trees and vegetable plots in the nearby shambas. The land then dropped rather more steeply and in the distance we could see the main buildings of the institute. However, it was the background which made the scene extraordinary, for there in the distance Lake Kivu nestled like a blue jewel in the green hills of the Albertine rift valley. 'It is beautiful, isn't it?' remarked Dr Kunkel. He explained that although it was appreciably colder than down near the main buildings he and his wife preferred to live up here. As well as enjoying magnificent scenery I was sure that he would also get more peace, for only the persistent would brave that road for any trivial matters!

I was shown through into their lounge, whose walls were hung with fine examples of native art of many forms: paintings, wood-carvings, masks, spears and other weapons. Large wooden chests and wardrobes, each deeply carved, stood against two of the walls. There were also three huge wooden cages, each covered on all sides by chicken wire. Two contained several bush babies while the third housed three pottos. To add to the menagerie a small cage near the doorway housed a 'tabby' kitten which was in fact a genuine wild cat. The whole atmosphere of the room was artistic, zoological and full of the excitement and mystery of Africa.

I was given a wonderful reception by the Kunkels. Formalities were quickly dispensed with and I was immediately on Christian name terms with Peter, his charming wife, Irene, and their two young sons, Andreas and Georg. I was instantly made to feel very much at home, and by meal time, when we all sat round the large, oval table in the dining room, I almost felt part of the family. Fortunately both Peter and Irene spoke excellent English so I was spared the embarrassment of practising my inadequate French except with the children. After dinner we were joined by two of the researchers from the ecological programme, Dr Gelmroth, who was studying rodents, and Dr Michael Casimir, who like myself was studying gorillas. There is nothing quite like a blazing log fire for giving a homely atmosphere, and sitting round it we talked far into the night about everything from biology to world politics – and, of course, gorillas. Michael Casimir was going into the forest the next day so I eagerly accepted his invitation to join him.

After an early breakfast next morning Michael drove up to Tshibati in his kombie to collect me. It felt strange to go into the field by car to see gorillas and even stranger when we reached the perfectly smooth stretch of tarmac road. I later discovered that it ran for over one hundred kilometres through the rain forest. The plan was that it would eventually reach Kisangani in the centre of Zaire, thus connecting the eastern and western provinces, but it was not yet completed. The road led uphill and was flanked on either side by neat rows of cultivated bananas. Scattered among them were wattle and daub houses. On the hillsides the bananas gave way to stands of eucalyptus trees and tea shrubs in the nearby plantations. A small crowd of Zairois were gathered at the side of the road leading to one of these plantations. They flagged us down and Michael stopped to pick them up. They were the trackers of M. Adrien Deschryver, the Park Conservator, who allowed them to work for Michael in tracking the gorillas. One, whose name was 'Pili-Pili' (Swahili for pepper!), was indeed a cheerful character and was obviously of pygmoid stock. Two others joined him in the kombie. Each wore long, black ex-army overcoats, which were several sizes too large for them, and carried sharp pangas. I had foolishly put on a navy coloured shirt and was already feeling far too hot, since at this altitude (2300 m.) temperatures were higher than I was used to in the volcanoes. The trackers, however, seemed comfortable in their greatcoats despite the blazing sunshine.

We drove on up the tarmac road and were soon inside the park itself, which covers some sixty thousand hectares of forest-covered hills and mountains near the south-westerly shores of Lake Kivu. Mts Kahuzi and Biega, both of volcanic origin, are two of the highest and most spectacular mountains in the area, and the park is named after them. Unlike many East African parks there was no gateway to pass through or office at which to register, just a simple blue and white sign announcing 'Parc National du Kahuzi-Biega'. Dense green forest reached to the very edge of the road, making the neat tarmac surface seem completely incongruous in such a setting. In some areas it was quite obvious that many of the trees were young and part of secondary regenerating growth. Other patches were of mature primary forest; some had giant trunks rising straight up and branch-free for over twenty metres before bursting out into a mighty crown of foliage in the canopy layer. The road climbed on higher and higher, and when we reached the top of a steep hill Michael pulled the kombie into the side of the road and parked on the grassy verge. 'This is kilometre thirty-four,' he said. 'We will leave the car here and enter the forest by one of the pygmies' trails over there.'

We quickly put on our boots and assembled our gear. One of the pygmies stayed behind to guard the car while the other two picked up our rucksacks and led the way into the forest. At this point the road passed through a steep cutting, and across the banks on either side were scattered masses of tall spindly stems capped by large, pure white lilies. Everywhere was peaceful and quiet. The pygmies passed through a tiny gap in the forest wall which was visible only to the experienced eye. However, as we passed through I could see that it was in fact a well-worn pathway. It led downhill through a tangled mass of secondary growth, no doubt the result of forest clearing when the roadway was built. I revelled in the cool, green freshness of the forest and filled my lungs with its many perfumes. Since the vegetation was so unlike that of the volcanoes it seemed rather unreal and somewhat eerie at first. I remembered that this was how I had felt on Mt Visoke, but later, when the forest was as familiar to me as my own garden, I felt equally at home there. To most visitors the tropical rain forest or 'jungle', be it lowland or montane, appears hostile and frightening. To the forest-dwellers, the pygmies, it is very much their home to which they are physiologically as well as ecologically and sociologically well adapted. It provides them with everything they need from the food they eat to the excitement they crave. Over countless generations they had become beautifully adapted to life in this seemingly hostile environment just as the antelopes or gorillas themselves had, or as other men had become adapted to life in deserts, savannahs, or polar regions. Before I left England I had read the beautiful and moving account of their lives by Colin Turnbull in his book *The Forest People* and had marvelled at the way he had come to know them by actually living with them in the forest. Our pygmies now chatted loudly to each other as we travelled through the forest. It was obvious that like many others these two had by now been greatly influenced by life outside the forest and no longer lived a traditional way of life.

We walked for several hours, up and down many hills and through several small swamps of tall papyrus reeds (*Cyperus latifolius*). Eventually the trackers picked up the gorilla trail from the previous day and we followed it until we reached the nest site where the gorillas had slept until dawn that day. I immediately noticed several obvious differences from the pattern of nesting behaviour I was familiar with in the Virunga volcanoes. First there were many more nests above the ground, but this could simply be because there were many more layers of shrubs and trees here than in the Virunga region. But not so easily explained was the fact that the copious amounts of dung voided by the gorillas during the night were not inside the nest, as was common in the Virungas, but were almost all outside the nest and therefore had not been slept on.

I pointed this out to Michael, recalling that Schaller had postulated that such differences in behaviour might be because the Virunga gorillas deposit larger quantities of dung than their counterparts in other regions. We agreed to investigate this to see if there was any truth in Schaller's hypothesis. Michael then mapped out the nest site just as I had done on Visoke. He explained that normally his work was complete when he had followed the trail to the nest site and documented his data on its layout. He suggested that to try to contact the gorillas would influence their normal movements about their home range. This, of course, is true but it means that one gets either no data at all about their behaviour or, at best, scraps of indirect evidence from the trail. I pointed out that Dian Fossey had extended Schaller's habituation techniques with obvious success and that after my research in Visoke I felt that while our contacts may have influenced the immediate movements of our study groups at the time of contact, they did not greatly influence the longer-term journeys. As the gorillas became more and more habituated so the influences of the observer became minimized. This was obviously not the ideal way to study their normal behaviour, but it was a good and well-tried compromise. I also pointed out the dangers of not making regular contacts, for then it was difficult to be sure that you were always following the trail of the same group. It would be all too easy to follow the trail of another group inadvertently if their tracks crossed those of your study animals.

Michael agreed to try to make a contact and we set off to follow the fresh tracks. The pygmies did not seem too pleased about this and muttered before somewhat grudgingly picking up the bags. Their keen eyes quickly picked up the fresh trail leading away from the nest site, and we followed them quietly. We walked for over an hour before one of them suddenly stopped and with a nod of his head murmured, 'They are over there.' We listened and soon could hear the sounds of branches being broken and vegetation being pulled down.

I signalled the trackers to come behind us and then slowly led the way along the fresh trail towards the feeding animals. We crept along quietly for about a hundred metres then paused again. All was now strangely quiet so I decided to wait. Suddenly a loud 'pok-a-pok-a-pok-a-pok' chest-beat rang out very close by. As I turned to smile at Michael Casimir and indicate that we had a contact, a loud roar pierced the stillness of the forest. This was followed by crackling of the vegetation as a huge body came crashing through it towards us. I automatically sat down and signalled Michael and the trackers to do the same, but the pygmies shook their heads and declined to do so. Fortunately the charging gorilla stopped just the other side of a dense clump of vegetation some three or four metres away. We could hear it breathing heavily. Then the vegetation crackled again, quietly this time, and I could hear the animal moving away from us.

We waited for fifteen minutes but all was still and quiet. I could see a better vantage point some twenty metres further along the trail. I signalled the trackers to stay where they were but told Michael to follow me. We crept forward slowly and quietly until we reached the spot I intended. We were at the top of a small rise and, as I hoped, could see a little way ahead through some gaps in the dense vegetation. I scanned all around through my binoculars, but could not see a single moving thing. I was just about to say aloud 'They have gone', when with a loud cracking and breaking of small branches, a young adult gorilla slid rapidly down a tree about fifteen metres in front of us. We watched him through our binoculars until he disappeared into the dense undergrowth around the base of the tree. He was followed by another, even smaller juvenile. I could see that Michael was now excited by this, his first sighting of his study animals. I hoped that we could see more but we waited in vain for a further fifteen minutes before faint noises in the distance indicated that the group had moved further on. I told Michael that by means of frequent contacts such as that even these animals could become habituated and observed, though I despaired at the dense vegetation which seemed to defy all attempts to see anything.

CHAPTER TEN

Deschryver's gorillas

Michael had arranged to meet Adrien Deschryver the next day for a formal introduction to one of his groups of habituated gorillas. I eagerly accepted his invitation to join them and so the following morning we again drove to meet the pygmy trackers. Deschryver was already there. A well-built man of medium height in his early thirties, he was quietly spoken and seemed rather reserved, especially at my unexpected presence. Once the introductions were over we drove on into the park, but this time to kilometre thirty-six. This was at a slightly higher altitude than kilometre thirty-four, and as we approached it the forest was suddenly replaced by the tall, willowy stems of bamboo forest. The vast monoculture of this giant member of the grass family, with its mature stems some ten centimetres in diameter and over ten metres tall, was pierced only by the occasional crowns of the giant *Polyscias fulva* trees which were scattered here and there like huge daisies in an immense lawn.

Again leaving someone to guard the cars we followed our guides along the winding trail. To me the peace and quiet of the forest is sacrosanct so I was disappointed to find that the pygmies again chatted loudly as we followed the well-trodden trail through the bamboo forest. Deftly they cut down any bamboos or vines which had fallen or grown over the trail. The noise of the metal pangas cutting through the tough bamboo stems sounded like rifle fire and I desperately wanted to shout for quiet. However, Adrien Deschryver himself did not seem to be perturbed so I forced myself to be patient.

Rather than follow the gorilla trail of the previous day the pygmies had decided to try and meet the gorillas from another direction. We therefore searched the area for fresh tracks and food remnants, but after over an hour we had still not found

143

anything. Suddenly a faint but familiar 'pok-a-pok-a-pok-a-pok' stopped me in my tracks. The keen ears of the pygmies had also heard this chest-beat and they began to jabber excitedly amongst themselves in a language I could not follow, and then consulted Deschryver in Swahili as to the best way to reach the gorillas we had just heard. He nodded his agreement and we set off again. I noticed a dramatic change in the atmosphere. The trackers now spoke rarely as they cut the track through the dense undergrowth. They paused to listen before carefully cutting the vegetation. Then, laying it gently on one side, they crept forward quietly. Soon we could hear branches being broken ahead and our movements became even more cautious.

After about twenty minutes of travelling in this way the noises stopped, and so then did we. Adrien looked at his watch. 'It is twelve o'clock,' he said, 'they will rest until two o'clock, so we will have to wait.' I was surprised by his confidence in making such a statement, but we settled down to rest, eat our lunch and talk until he decided it was time to continue.

I asked Adrien what had prompted him to undertake such a formidable task as trying to habituate wild gorillas. He shrugged his broad shoulders and explained that he had lived most of his life in this area and when old enough he began to hunt antelopes, wild pigs and even elephants in these forests. As the years passed by he had become deeply impressed by gorillas and their way of life in the forest. As he spoke I wondered whether this was because he himself was so obviously more at home in this forest world than in the outside world of commercialism. He went on to explain that the Kahuzi-Biega area was given Forest Reserve status in 1960 and he became personally responsible for it in 1966. Realizing that it was urgent to save the forests from being claimed by the advancing agriculture in this densely populated area he decided to explore the possibility of using the gorillas as a tourist attraction. Thus he hoped to gain both national and international recognition, and the funds which were vital to the reserve's continued existence. Obviously tourists would not only demand a safe safari, but also one which guaranteed good views of gorillas, therefore the gorillas had to be habituated to the presence of man.

I nodded in sympathy and understanding as he told me that the whole process was a long and frustrating one. He had first tried to contact the gorillas in 1966, but his work was interrupted by the upheaval in the Kivu area in 1967. In May 1968 he had started again. However, owing to his commitments of organizing anti-poaching patrols and general park administration duties he was only able to visit the gorillas four or five times each month. He found that they were so difficult to observe that it was over a year before he finally had a good sighting and this was due to a lucky encounter in a fairly open area of forest. After this he gradually saw more and more of the animals of two family groups. He himself became bolder and whenever he contacted the gorillas he slowly cleared some of the vegetation in a circle around himself. While he did so he spoke to the gorillas and so, not only were they eventually prepared for the inevitable chatter of tourists, but also they got used to his voice. He found that the flattened vegetation made observations easier, and it also made things safer since the adult males seemed reluctant to charge across such an open place. His efforts were finally recognized when, in November 1970, the Kahuzi-Biega forest reserve was given the status of a National Park.

I asked him why he carried such a large and conspicuous rifle when Schaller had stressed the importance of not being armed (in addition to not speaking aloud!). Deschryver laughed and said, 'This rifle has been the key to my success, for it has given me the necessary confidence to carry out this habituation in such dense forest as you have seen today. Without my rifle,' he continued, 'I am very afraid of the gorillas – even more than you are!' He explained that as a hunter he always carried a rifle when in the forest and especially when on safari, as it gave confidence and reassurance to the tourists. 'It is a very special rifle,' he said while almost caressing the shining weapon. 'I had to order it from Belgium. You see, if a gorilla charged me in this dense forest and I was armed with a normal bolt-action rifle then I would probably shoot to kill if it came too close, for I would not get time for a second shot. This rifle, however, is a very powerful automatic and therefore I can first shoot at the ground in front of the charging animal and then, instantly if necessary, shoot to kill.' With justifiable pride he went on to say that in six years he had never fired a single shot, though he had *almost* fired on several occasions.

I could have listened all day to Adrien's tales and as two o'clock got nearer I thought to myself that we would end up doing just that. However, incredibly, at precisely 1.59 p.m. I heard some faint crackling in the vegetation, and by exactly 2.00 p.m. the sounds of many bamboos being broken rang through the forest! Adrien did not say a word, until at 2.15 p.m. he turned to the pygmies. 'Tegende' (let us go), he said softly, and off we went.

We again travelled quietly and slowly, pausing frequently to listen. We could hear that the gorillas were only slightly ahead of us. Suddenly a large male roared and crashed through the dense vegetation about twenty metres away. A smile lit up the hitherto serious face of Adrien. 'Now we have a contact,' he said. Then, to my amazement, he raised his head and shouted loudly, 'Come, come, come-come, come!' The male gorilla roared again and once more crashed through the vegetation. 'Climb up this tree and you should be able to see better,' Adrien said. So with the help of a mighty push, Casimir and I scrambled and crashed our way through the dense canopy of vines entwining the small tree. Despite moving out on to a side branch, I could only see vague movements ahead and below me.

'There's the big male,' Adrien said. 'I have cleared some of the vegetation now. Come down here and you can see him.' We clambered down again, while Adrien shouted, 'Come, come, come, Bwana mkubwa come.' He had cut down a lot of the vines with his pocket knife and made a large hole in the dense vegetation. I peered into the gloom, but could not make anything out clearly. 'Look along the barrel of my rifle,' Adrien said, and to my horror he raised his rifle and stuck it straight out. Not knowing quite what to expect now, from either Adrien or the gorilla, I did so, and as my eyes accommodated to the gloom, the thing that I had taken for a tree stump moved, then roared loudly.

Bamboo stems were now being crashed and broken nearer

and nearer to us, and then I suddenly realized that not only were the gorillas coming closer, but that they were feeding on the way! Some of the group actually came to within four or five metres and I was able to observe how they fed on the new bamboo shoots in this dense forest. Furthermore, I was able to move around, though slowly, in order to observe several animals, from different positions, as they moved and fed nearby. After about half an hour the group began to move away, feeding as they travelled through the bamboos, until even their noises faded away. Reluctantly I picked up my rucksack and we retraced our tracks. As we returned along the trail towards the car we heard the big male roar again, and this convinced me that I had not been dreaming, but that this somewhat bizarre expedition by Visoke standards had given me some unique observations which I would not have believed possible in such dense forest. Before we parted I thanked Adrien profusely and congratulated him on his unique work. He had undoubtedly laid the vital foundations for the scientific work which Michael Casimir was now starting.

I remained in Zaire for a week, during which time I met and talked to many other members of the institute staff and made a memorable visit to the tiny field station at Irangi in the equatorial forest. After the pleasant climate in the high mountain rain forest I found the hot, humid air of the lowland forest overpowering and this, coupled with the rapid descent from the mountains, made me feel lethargic. However, I was still able to manage a walk along a shallow river bed to view a mighty waterfall where the main river tumbled downwards to join the Zaire (Congo) river on its immense journey first north and then westwards to the South Atlantic ocean.

The differences in the wildlife between this area and the mountain forest were truly remarkable, especially in the numbers and variety of its birds, spiders, butterflies and other insects. A streak of bright tropical sunlight pierced the dense forest above the river bed, and constantly flitting in and out of its light were countless numbers of multicoloured and iridescent butterflies of all shapes and sizes. These were chased by equally

brightly coloured birds. Here and there were large spiders'
webs bejewelled with drops of moisture from the saturated air.
Myriads of ants of several species made their pilgrimages
through the dense leaf litter underfoot, while on a nearby tree
was a one-metre-high termite nest, its layers of steeply pitched
rain roofs making it look like a miniature pagoda. This was
indeed the active, life- and death-filled 'jungle'.

I climbed up the thirty-metre-high tower and along the rope
and wood bridges which the IRSAC staff had constructed in
order to study, amongst other things, the new species of rats and
mice they had recently discovered living in this arboreal world.
As I looked down from the top of the canopy I could not see
through the dense foliage to the ground below. The huge
crowns were so densely packed together that it was impossible
to say where one tree ended and another began. Thus, lacking
any visual clues as to my true height above ground, I could
foolishly have attempted to step out into this dense carpet of
leaves. It was exciting, and rather frightening, to walk along the
shaky bridges trying to convince yourself that you really were so
high and that the new nylon rope of the bridges really was
strong. In the sea of countless hues of green one tree stood out
with its mass of bright red blossom. This spectacular view of the
forest made me realize more than anything else just how three-
dimensional the forest world really is, and what a narrow view
of it we mere humans normally obtain. It was in fact the
presence of these many layers, each a slightly different environment, which created the multitude of ecological niches for both
plants and animals to exploit, thus increasing their variety and
complexity.

Soon I had another aerial view of this forest world, but this
time from a distance as my plane winged northwards over the
calm waters of Lake Kivu towards Goma. I was very pleased
with my trip to IRSAC and felt that I had made many friends
who had helped me, and whom in turn I had been able to help.
In particular I had discussed my research programme in detail
with Michael Casimir. Being new to the field station he had felt
exactly as I had done during my first few weeks at Visoke – overwhelmed by the multitude of problems and convinced that

previous workers, notably Schaller, had already done 'everything'. I later discovered that this was a common phobia among most research students, whether studying in the field or in the lab. I therefore showed Michael my prepared research schemes and we agreed to try and compare our findings when our respective studies were completed.

Away from the friendly atmosphere of IRSAC I now wondered again whether my own project would in fact be allowed to continue. I had sent a telegram to Dian to warn her of the date and time of my arrival but I was now filled with trepidation in case my journey would be in vain. I discovered that I was too late to travel to Ruhengeri that day for the bus from Gisenyi had already left. Fortunately I was able to stay with Francis and Else Dondeyne, who made me most welcome. We exchanged news and discussed the events which had taken place since our departure, including a spectacular 'minor' eruption of Nyiragongo, one of the active volcanoes in the Virunga chain, just after we had left.

To my pleasant surprise I also discovered that Mtoto, my chimpanzee 'son', was still in Gisenyi. In fact he was in a nearby garden. It transpired that when my own efforts to find him a home had failed, Dian had given him to a European in Gisenyi. I hurried there to see him. As I approached up the pathway I could see him sitting on a low wall. He was tethered by a long chain which was fastened to the same dog collar which I had put on him nearly a year earlier. He started to scream as I got nearer. I paused and gently murmured, 'Mtoto, Mtoto, come here, Mtoto.' He immediately stopped screaming, climbed off the wall, and approached me with an air of suspicion. When he was just a few metres away I bent down and stretched out my arms towards him. With an excited 'Ugh! Ugh! Ugh!' of recognition he raced into my open arms and clung tightly to my chest, just as he had done over six months earlier. It was one of the most dramatic and moving experiences of my life and tears welled up in my eyes at the thought that he still recognized me after all this time. I played with him for almost an hour before I finally had to tear myself away, once more to his heart-piercing screams of anguish at being deserted. Saddened and frustrated, I realized there was now nothing that I could do that would make matters better for him. All my good intentions had failed and he was once more a prisoner in Gisenyi. 'How much better it is,' I thought, 'that animals like these remain in the forest where they make friends with humans only if they so desire and are free to follow their natural lives.' That was the last I ever saw of Mtoto. I hope he found a good home and a more reliable 'mother substitute' than myself.

Early the next morning I boarded the bus for Ruhengeri. It was obviously unusual for Europeans to travel by bus for I was the only one among a crowd of local inhabitants who stared at me in astonishment. Their faces lit up with delight when I smiled and murmured, 'Mraho, Mraho.' However, I avoided any further conversation lest they should discover the limit of my Kinyarwandan vocabulary!

The journey to Ruhengeri was even worse by bus than it was by car, and I arrived feeling shaken to pieces. There was no sign of either Bob or Dian. I decided to go to see Verma, the local Asian merchant who had often helped me before. He made me welcome but unfortunately he could not give me news of Dian for he had not seen her for several weeks. However, he told me that my luggage was in his store-room for Dian had sent it down from camp some months earlier. This seemed an ominous sign.

Realizing my plight he kindly offered to get his driver to take me to where the kombie was normally parked. Then I could walk up the familiar trail to camp – but I had to wait until late in the afternoon before the driver could leave. As we drove out of Ruhengeri clouds were rolling down the sides of the nearby volcanoes. We were in for a storm. Fortunately it was only short, for it broke and passed while we climbed up the winding road through the shambas. The pyrethrum was now well grown and vast stretches of the large white daisy-like flowers were abundant on both sides of the road all the way up the mountainside. We finally reached the parking space, and I gave my driver a well-earned *matabeeshi* and bade him a safe return to Ruhengeri. Meanwhile I gave my bag to a willing porter and we climbed the rain-drenched trail.

When I reached camp I was first greeted by Cindy, and, of

course, Kima. Nemeye was at camp and came to shake hands, his face beaming with sincere delight. Unfortunately Kanyura-guana was down the mountain on leave at home. The camp had changed somewhat during our absence. Dian had moved into the upper cabin and Bob Campbell, no doubt tired of tent life, had built himself a prefabricated cabin nearby. After a cool reception Dian explained that my telegram, sent a week earlier from IRSAC, a mere sixty miles away, had only just arrived. However, the men had lit a fire in the lower cabin and made up a bed for me. I was invited to join Dian and Bob for dinner so I went to change out of my wet boots and jeans. During the meal Dian made it quite obvious that she did not wish me to remain at the camp, though I was told I could work from a tented camp at Ngezi on the east side of Visoke if I signed the letter of agreement first. I explained my position regarding Liverpool University's attitude to the wording of this agreement, but Dian was adamant.

I went to bed that night troubled that our relationship, once so good, had deteriorated so much. I decided to visit Ngezi the following day with Nemeye to view its possibilities as a research site; it was, indeed, a lovely area, but to work there would mean virtually to start again from the beginning. My previous data on Groups 4, 5, 8 and 9 could not now be extended and I would therefore have to find another family group suitable for my proposed research, which I had hoped to continue with either Group 4 or 5. Effectively my plans, my project and my hopes were now dead.

I left camp the following day in extremely low spirits and the trip down the mountain was cheered up only by meeting Kanyuraguana. Bob Campbell kindly drove me to Ruhengeri in his Land-Rover, where I went straight to Verma's and set about packing up our belongings to ship them home. I gave away heavy, unessential items to reduce the weight as much as possible. Verma, friendly and hospitable as ever, kindly let me stay the night with him and his family, for the local hotel was closed. Early the next morning I boarded the bus for Gisenyi. Everything now seemed empty and remote and I felt an unwelcome intruder into the world of my fellow passengers.

At Gisenyi I called in to say goodbye to Francis and Else before visiting the nearby Sabena office to book my flight to Europe. Francis was almost as disappointed as myself by the sad turn of events, for he had been to visit me on Visoke and was enthralled by the entire gorilla research programme. He said that it would be foolish for me to go directly back to England and suggested that I first returned to see Dr Kunkel at IRSAC. I pointed out that if I did go Michael Casimir would feel that his newly acquired scientific territory was being poached, and that a similar situation to my present one could arise again. Francis and Else, however, insisted that I should at least *try* to see if there were any possibilities to study other gorillas at Kahuzi. Though I did not feel very optimistic I eventually agreed to their suggestions. I sent a telegram to Verma asking him not to despatch my luggage until he heard from me again; then, after spending another night with Francis and Else, I set off on the plane back to Bukavu. At Kavumu airport I got a taxi to take me to IRSAC. As we approached the institute I became more and more apprehensive and convinced that this journey, like my trip to Visoke, was rather futile. Peter Kunkel had left the institute for Tshibati, so my worries were further prolonged while the taxi drove me up the winding hillside road to his house.

Though somewhat astonished, Peter welcomed me back to IRSAC. I explained the situation, and he listened sympathetically and in complete understanding. He laughed at my suggestion that it could happen again and said, 'We shall see, we shall see, leave it to me!' Like Francis and Else he insisted that I did not think about returning home, and astonished me by saying that I should get Margaret and Fiona out to IRSAC as soon as possible. I am sure that from his own experiences of Africa he had long since realized the importance of boosting people's morale. He told me to write home immediately while he set about finding me some permanent accommodation and obtaining the necessary permits and visas for me to stay. His reassuring air made all the problems appear to diminish but neither he nor I knew the troubles we were to have even in obtaining the necessary work permits.

Peter clearly had to find some research possibilities for me without offending Michael Casimir, who, as I suspected, was not too pleased at my return. After an abortive trip to try and find gorillas in the lowland forest near Walikale, further west than I had already been at Irangi, Peter decided that we should go and discuss the problems with Adrien Deschryver and ask for his advice. To my delight Adrien immediately agreed that I could work within the Kahuzi-Biega National Park. He suggested that I could look for gorillas in the forest surrounding his guards' camp at Mukaba, near kilometre 49 on the tarmac road. He was somewhat amused, however, and warned me that the gorillas of this area were 'wild' and not like the two groups which he often contacted. 'Oh! they cannot be any worse than Group Eight on Mount Visoke,' I said confidently. Little did I know how wrong I was!

Now elated at the prospects, I set about getting organized and wrote to everyone concerned. Fortunately Professor Cain was able to persuade the Science Research Council to transfer my NATO research studentship to IRSAC. Meanwhile Peter Kunkel was busy arranging accommodation and obtaining a vehicle for my use. Francis and Else Dondeyne were naturally pleased that things had turned out so well. Margaret, however, was more realistic, and, although she promised to travel to Zaire as soon as possible, kept on asking if I had actually found any gorillas to study!

This I was busy trying to do. I first spent a week searching the forests around Mukaba with the aid of a local guide from the guard post, but although we found a few trail signs they were up to twelve months old. We neither saw, nor even heard, the gorillas themselves. I began to suspect that these forests, of mainly primary vegetation, were poor feeding grounds and were therefore only used occasionally, or perhaps by lone animals or small groups which were in transit from one area to another.

I then heard reports that gorillas had been seen a few kilometres away along the road to the village of Nyakalonge. At the institute I examined aerial photographs of the area which had been taken by the Institut Géographique du Congo Belge in

1958. I could see a roadway leading from the tarmac road, near kilometre 45, which travelled right through the forest and on to the open area of shambas at Nyakalonge. It seemed an ideal place to search, for if gorillas were in the area at some time or other they would have to cross that roadway. But what I now needed were good trackers, and this was how I came to meet yet another of the remarkable people who helped so much with my research: Patrice Wazi-Wazi.

CHAPTER ELEVEN

Tracking with Patrice the pygmy

I shall never forget my first meeting with Patrice. I had let it be known via Adrien's men that I wanted to employ two more trackers for my own work. I told them to tell anyone who was interested to come to our usual picking-up spot near the entrance to the tea plantation early the next morning. After breakfast the next day I drove out of IRSAC's gate convinced that things would now go well.

Feeling elated I drove towards Kahuzi, but as I approached the usual meeting place I saw an enormous crowd and I feared that an accident had taken place. I stopped the kombie and got out to investigate, whereupon I was immediately surrounded by a veritable mob of over a hundred shouting 'Bwana, Bwana, kazi, kazi' (work, work!). I saw Pili-Pili and the other trackers and realized that the word had, indeed, been spread around, for there were obviously more men here than from the two nearby pygmy encampments. How on earth was I to pick the best two trackers out of this lot?

Some of the men were obviously either too old or too ill to work, so I picked out two younger ones who looked fit enough for the many days of hard tracking ahead, and yet who were old enough to have had some experience of the forest. Another, whom I had passed by, was most persistent and kept insisting, 'Bwana, Bwana, I want work.' He was much smaller than the rest and his tiny spindly legs did not look as though they could carry him far. He looked old, I guessed between forty and fifty, though it was very hard to tell for he seemed ill. He kept muttering to me, 'Chef, Chef,' over and over again. I had thought he was calling me 'Chief' to be ultra polite, then I suddenly realized what he meant. He was the chief of the pygmies!

To be diplomatic I felt that I had to employ the chief so I finally agreed. I then decided to pick a fourth, explaining that all would have work for a while but that I would later pick out the best two for permanent work. In the year that followed I was to have many arguments with my trackers about their unwillingness to work, and many were sacked and others hired, but the little one, Patrice Wazi-Wazi, stayed with me until the day I left. From him I learned to view the forest and its inhabitants in a completely new way, and for this I shall always be grateful.

With my four new assistants, I scrambled out of the pressing crowd and retreated to the safety of the kombie. Each of the men now had broad grins of success, while their friends stared sorrowfully at me murmuring, 'Kazi, Bwana, kazi, kazi, kazi, kazi.' The word continued to ring in my ears as I drove away and stayed there long after even those who ran alongside the kombie had fallen behind.

We soon reached the road to Nyakalonge which looked no more than a dirt track. It led steeply down from the main tarmac road near kilometre 45. I had scarcely noticed it when previously passing on to Mukaba. However, I had now studied the aerial survey photographs in great detail using the institute's stereoscopic viewer so I was more familiar with the terrain. Although it was fourteen years since the aerial survey had been made the vegetation appeared to have changed little. Leaving the kombie at the side of the main road, we travelled on foot, looking for signs of gorillas on either side. The roadway wound westwards round the slopes of the foothills of Mt Kahuzi. At first it appeared to pass along the lower boundary of the bamboo forest which started abruptly at approximately 2500 metres. No doubt the road builders had skirted the steeper bamboo-covered slopes deliberately, preferring to wind back and forth around the hills rather than cross them directly. I wondered why this was so for the local inhabitants were well used to climbing up and down such steep hills. When later I saw a timber lorry floundering in the wet mud even on one of the gentler slopes the reason became obvious.

The tall waving stems of bamboo, at first overshadowing the

road on both sides, soon gave way on the lower side to montane rain forest. At the edge of the road itself, especially in the more open areas where plenty of sunlight got through, were patches of herbs and rampant vines. Some I recognized from the Virunga region such as *Galium, Carex* sedges and *Helichrysum* or 'everlasting flowers'. Others looked vaguely familiar, though from where I could not decide. Then I suddenly realized that here, growing in profusion, were the clematis, begonias and 'black-eyed Susans' that Margaret had struggled to cultivate at home.

Behind the roadside herbs was the forest itself. Here and there were trees typical of secondary regenerating growth such as *Neoboutonia macrocalyx* and *Dombeya goetzenii*. Their large dinner-plate sized leaves were virtually indistinguishable from each other except to the sharp eyes of the pygmies, who pointed out the distinguishing red leaf veins of *Dombeya*. Although many of these trees were over twenty years old and fully mature, their maximum height of some twenty metres was dwarfed by the nearby giants of the true primary montane forest on the lower side of the road. From the roadway it was easy to see why little light ever reached ground level through the closely interlocking canopy layer. Where it did, usually when a forest giant was felled by wind or lightning or by natural decay, the invading secondary forest burst forth with a profusion of rampant vines and shrubs. Among these would grow a sapling of a primary forest giant. Eventually it would dwarf the secondary forest plants and, as their precious life-giving sunlight faded, so then would their growth.

I discovered that each of the trees and, indeed, most of the plants had local names, and Patrice seemed to be an authority on their classification. This proved to be a most fortunate piece of luck for it not only enabled me to get many specimens identified quickly at the herbarium back at IRSAC but it meant that Patrice could give me on-the-spot identification of many plants. From him I learned the local names and later when I checked their identification I learned the scientific ones. Therefore as my experience of the forest grew so did my local and scientific lists of plant names.

We walked slowly along the road. Two trackers scrutinized

the slopes on either side and stopped here and there to investigate thoroughly every disturbed patch of vegetation. I noticed that Patrice's advice was always called for whenever there was a discussion. This did not seem to be in deference to his social standing, for he would carefully examine all the trail signs himself, sometimes disappearing for ten minutes or more before returning to shake his head at my enquiring look.

Progressing slowly it took us over two hours to explore three kilometres of road. We found numerous tracks of bush pig, antelopes, and even signs of the occasional terrestrial forays of the blue monkey, *Cercopithecus mitis*, but of our true quarry there was not a sign. We plodded slowly on for I was convinced that this was a good and convenient way to survey the area. Then we met some villagers travelling from Nyakalonge on their long walk to the market at Bukavu, almost fifty kilometres away. Each carried a large basket filled with goods to be sold.

My trackers and the villagers exchanged friendly and prolonged greetings. I asked Patrice to ask them if they had ever seen any signs of gorillas near this road. He replied that he already had asked them and they had not only seen gorilla signs but had heard the gorillas themselves, and that was *today*, just one kilometre along the road! I thanked them profusely, giving several packets of cigarettes as a *matabeeshi*, and we hurried on. I could see that the trackers were almost as excited as I was.

We soon reached the spot described by the villagers, and I could hardly believe my eyes. The roadway at this point was quite wide with a verge on the lower side covered in herbs and vines. Much of these had been trampled down and several eaten. One I recognized as a species of elephant grass, *Pennisetum*, and another of dock, *Rumex*. Patrice examined the broken stems and announced excitedly, 'They passed just now.' It seemed that the villagers may well have disturbed the gorillas in their roadside feast! Whilst thanking my luck I could not help wishing that it had been ourselves who had stumbled upon this feeding place.

However, this was the lucky break I needed so I had to take full advantage of it and try and make a contact straight away.

We examined the trail carefully and it was soon obvious that the gorillas had travelled down from the upper slopes above the road, then upon reaching the road itself they had wandered along the verge for over a hundred metres, feeding on the abundant plants among the secondary vegetation. We found the spot where they had left the road, presumably when they heard the villagers approaching. It led downhill through the dense primary forest.

Leaving two of the trackers behind I followed the fresh trail accompanied by Patrice and one of the younger pygmies. We had only travelled about fifty paces when a loud alarm bark, followed immediately by an even louder scream, shattered the silence of the forest. I stopped immediately and out of habit I sat down, motioning my trackers to do the same. This they did and we sat perfectly still listening carefully for indications of exactly where the gorillas were located. The vegetation all around us made it unbelievably dark. Although it had not yet rained everything was soaking wet to the touch making sitting down extremely uncomfortable. The vegetation had muffled even the loud scream but I had judged the gorillas to be only some forty metres away.

Three minutes passed slowly, then there was another loud alarm bark, and four minutes later came a third. This time it was full of alarm and verged on a scream. It was followed by a loud ground thump which sounded most impressive despite the muffling effect of the forest. I scanned the vegetation ahead through my binoculars but could only see for some ten metres at the most through some tiny gaps between the trees and shrubs. Another alarm bark rang out. This time it appeared to be more like the 'questioning bark' I was familiar with from the Visoke gorillas. This was followed by another two-beat ground thump, then three minutes later I heard a faint throat-clearing noise.

I sat quietly and just waited to see what would happen. During the next thirty minutes there were four more alarm barks at varying intervals. These were punctuated by two more sets of ground thumps and the breaking of a shrub or small tree. However, there was no sign of the gorillas themselves or, indeed, of any movement. I therefore decided to try and arouse their interest by giving a few gentle chest-beats by slapping my hands quietly on my thigh.

There was no immediate response but a minute later another loud alarm bark rang out, this time from further away. It seemed to fade into a questioning bark, though not as clear as those with which I was familiar and I wondered whether these were regional gorilla dialects. I waited a few minutes then gave a few more quiet chest-beat imitations. Again there was no response. I waited for another ten minutes but all was now quiet in the forest. I decided to retreat and indicated to the trackers to do so quietly. With scarcely a sound we began to creep back uphill. Another alarm bark indicated that the keen ears of the silverback had detected even these tiny movements. We moved even slower in order not to upset him.

Returning to the roadside I walked quietly up and down carefully listening for any tell-tale signs which would give away the gorillas' location. All was still quiet and the gloomy, primary forest defied all my attempts to see more than a few metres inside. On the steep slope the crowns of the trees were layered one behind and slightly below the other making an impenetrable black wall. The forest dipped down to the huge swamp, the 'Musisi', a few hundred metres below. This enormous area, over eight kilometres long and in places over four kilometres wide, at an altitude of 2300 m., was the remains of an ancient lake. On the aerial photos it appeared like an elongated amoeba sending out many false feet, especially at its northern and southern tips. At a much later period in geological time the waters had been replaced during natural ecological succession by a complete cover of papyrus (*Cyperus latifolius*) reeds. At some far distant period in the future these, too, would be replaced by the forest trees which had already colonized some of the drier patches of the swamp.

I wondered whether this group actually went into the swamp or even travelled right across to the forested hills on its eastern side. I had thought of searching over there but it seemed too close to Michael Casimir's study area. I therefore hoped that this newly found group confined their ranging activities to its western side.

I examined the trail left by the feeding animals carefully and collected specimens of the plants they had eaten and those nearby which had not been touched. It was important for me to discover which plants the gorillas did not eat as well as those they did eat. By making daily records of the plants eaten, their local abundance and the general vegetation type in which they were found, I hoped to build up a picture of the gorillas' food repertoire and their preferences, if any, for particular plants.

I decided to back-track the gorillas' trail to find their nest site, so that I could determine the size and composition of the group. Here I first came across one of the biggest difficulties of working in primary forest, that of following the gorillas' tracks. In places like the roadside, where there was an almost complete ground cover of herbs, this was extremely easy. Trampled stems and withering leaves gave ample clues for even a novice to follow. However, under the shade of the primary forest giants tracking was a very different matter and tested even the skill of the pygmies to the limit. For here there were few, if any, herbs to be crushed underfoot. Many areas in fact were completely bare and only tiny tell-tale marks on the soil indicated the gorillas' route. In patches of leaf and twig litter even these disappeared, but the sharp eyes of the trackers searched for freshly made depressions in the springy surface.

If they lost the trail all four would fan out often in a complete circle. A low whistle indicated that one of them had found the elusive tracks. It was exciting to see them work and I once more envied Colin Turnbull's adventures with the pygmies of the Ituri forest on their hunting expeditions.

Such tracking made progress painfully slow and this was even slower when we had to cut our way through patches of tangled vines and shrubs. It seemed unbelievable that animals as large as gorillas could possibly have passed through such vegetation and once I ventured to voice my doubts to the pygmies. His pride obviously hurt, Patrice disdainfully pointed out tell-tale signs which my inexperienced eyes had not seen. Sure enough, when we had hacked our way through, there was the occasional knuckle-print or partial foot-print on the damp bare soil or a minute depression in the leaf litter. All were blatantly obvious – when pointed out!

For over an hour we plodded on, then the trail turned up towards the bamboo forest. Here tracking became even more difficult, for a thick layer of bamboo leaves covered almost the entire ground. Their springy texture hid almost all tracks, even those of the pygmies walking immediately in front of me. To make matters worse it started to rain.

We had covered well over a kilometre yet had not seen a single sign of feeding by the gorillas since we had left the road-side. Indeed, I was wondering what they would find to eat in this mature forest for little grew at ground level. Even the bamboo shoots were now almost fully grown and hard. None appeared to have been touched. We plodded on, the rain got heavier and heavier, then the storm unleashed its full force and a veritable wall of water descended on us.

We looked around for a place to shelter. The massive trunks of the primary forest giants rose straight as pillars towards the sky far above. Here I would find no hospitable twisted shapes of the *Hagenia* trees which had given me so much shelter on Mt Visoke. Pushing our way into a tangle of hanging vines around one goliath we pressed ourselves as close to the trunk as possible. Much to the surprise and amusement of the pygmies I brought out my latest defence against tropical downpours, a collapsible umbrella. Unfortunately, the tiny green area of nylon was hardly sufficient to protect all five of us and there was much friendly pushing and shoving to stay under its cover. After half an hour, thoroughly soaked, we decided it would be better to go back in the rain rather than wait goodness knows how long for it to stop. All the small signs of the gorilla trail had long since been obliterated by the torrential downpour.

When we reached the road the pygmies made their own improvised umbrellas. Each of them cut a huge leaf from a wild banana plant and held it above his head spiked on his panga. My own clothes had got wet before I had reluctantly put on my waterproofs, for then I got even wetter with condensation, but at least I was warm. None of them had a coat or even a sweater. Their shirts and trousers were tattered remnants of European clothing and nothing, not even one pair of trousers between them, was intact. Patrice's shorts were from a pair of ancient cut-down flannels. I resolved to get them some clothes from the market at Kavumu the next day and, as soon as possible, some waterproofs. After our walk in the forest the five kilometres back along the unmade road were rather dreary, especially in the rain. We were all relieved to climb up the last slope and fall wet and exhausted into the kombie.

The next morning I bought four coats in the market and, to their delight, I gave one each to the pygmies. There had been little variety to choose from and I had chosen the sturdiest I could find, and also the smallest. However, even these looked enormous on their tiny frames and I had to hide my amusement as they paraded themselves up and down the road, intensely proud of their new acquisitions.

Patrice in particular looked a comical sight. I had given him a three-quarter imitation suede jacket with fleecy lining. Since he was by far the smallest of the four, only some four feet nine inches tall (one and a half metres), the coat came down past his knees making his spindly legs look even more like two brown matchsticks. On his head he wore the crowning glory, a shiny black sou'wester! I had brought some spare ones with me intending to give them to Nemeye and Munya on Visoke. Now Patrice and one of his friends were busy showing them off to the onlooking crowd. Their outfits looked even more out of place because the morning sky was now perfectly clear and the sun shone warmly on the roadside pantomime. Nevertheless, each tracker proudly wore his new coat and sou'wester as he climbed aboard the kombie to go to work.

To save the extra walk I decided to risk taking the kombie along the unmade road to Nyakalonge. Despite skidding through one large muddy area we managed to reach a suitable place to park. Then we set off to follow the previous day's trail after the gorillas. Again tracking was frustrating, as the trail signs varied from blatantly obvious to faint and obscure. First we climbed down the steep hillside until we reached a river which ran through the bottom of a valley. This was the river Luka, which meandered through the centre of the swamp for half its length before suddenly turning westwards into the forest. After collecting the run-off from the nearby slopes of Kahuzi and the numerous smaller hills it travelled on westwards into the giant network of rivers feeding the mighty Zaire (Congo) river itself.

At this spot the river was only two or three metres wide and in parts only fifty centimetres deep. The gorillas' trail ran alongside it for several hundred metres then crossed it over a fallen log. I recalled that Schaller had noted the apparent aversion of gorillas to crossing water, even shallow streams such as this. He had therefore postulated, quite reasonably, that since gorillas do not appear to be able to swim, their geographic range is limited by rivers which are too wide to be bridged by fallen trees; thus there were not thought to be any gorillas inside the large Zaire river basin itself. The headwaters of the Zaire (as the Lualaba) could have provided a crossing place, but were further south than the known gorilla range. Schaller's hypothesis was that the gorillas had originated in West Africa during the early Pleistocene and were able to extend their range eastwards via the belt of rain forest which was present north of the Zaire river at that time. They then colonized the lowland and montane forest area east of the Lualaba. He argued that the present day distribution in the eastern regions, which was over an area shaped like an inverted triangle, supported the hypothesis that the animals had started to colonize the forest from the north, where they were now more widespread than in the south.

The gorilla trail followed the eastern bank of the river for a hundred metres or so then crossed back to the western bank over another fallen log. Why the gorillas had crossed back, or, indeed, why they had crossed in the first place, I could not tell, for once again there were no signs of feeding. With the aid of a tiny counter I was recording the number of paces we had travelled since we left the road. When the counter showed 1260 paces the gorilla trail turned away from the river and headed back uphill in a diagonal path towards the roadway.

Less than fifty paces further on we found a small clearing where several trees had long since fallen and now lay covered in masses of secondary growth. Here I found the first sign of feeding, on the bark of a small shrub which Patrice called 'Chichorshe'. It looked similar to the *Vernonia adolphi-frederici* on Visoke and later identification showed it to be a member of the same genus but a different species, *Vernonia jugalis*. Nearby were scattered dozens of pieces of the peeled stem of a thin woody vine which Patrice called 'Mushe'. This was my first real encounter with the plant, whose scientific name is *Urera hypselodendron*, which I was to record later as the major item in the daily diet of the gorillas in the Kahuzi forests.

Further on the same trail there were more tell-tale piles of peeled 'Mushe' stems. Each had been either bitten or broken off the main vine and were between one and two metres long. Scattered among the browning stems were piles of the heart-shaped leaves, which the feeding gorillas had pulled off and discarded before eating the bark. Samples of other food items were added to my list and specimens taken for positive identification. Patrice again provided local names, 'Tshinono' (*Serico-stachys scandens*), 'Muberenaga' (*Rumex abyssinica*), 'Irere' (*Begonia* sp.) and 'Mushegemanjoca' (*Piper capense*). Each rolled carefully off his tongue with an exact and authoritative air after he had carefully examined the leaves and bark, or even smelled their aroma.

I never ceased to be impressed by Patrice's botanical expertise, which by far overshadowed the attempts of the other trackers. I even tested him in the herbarium at IRSAC, where to the delight of the botanist, Jean Ntakiyimana, who identified most of my specimens, Patrice proved to be both consistent and accurate in his identifications. We could not even trick him by presenting several different specimens from the same species, although some were in flower and others were not. We did confirm, however, what I had suspected in the forest, that despite the many and varied names the pygmies have for the multitude of forest plants some plants share the same name. In several cases these were of several species within the one genus, e.g. all *Cissus* species were called 'Muhulula' and all *Lactuca* species 'Luvunanga'. Unfortunately their consistency was not perfect, for several other plants from different genera also came under the name Muhulula, while 'Gahura' covered all plants exuding a sticky white latex. Thus like our own biological classificatory system the pygmies grouped together specimens by their similarities, but unlike us they were not too concerned with any minute differences which serve to set the many animals and plant species apart.

As well as recording the plants which the gorillas ate I also took colour photographs of the vegetation in which they were found, which slowed our progress again; thus it took several hours to cover the 2084 paces to the nest site. Taking into consideration the distance I had covered back-tracking the previous day (unfortunately without finding the nest site) the gorillas must have travelled at least three kilometres in one day. Since this was more than twice the longest day-journey I had recorded for the study groups on Mt Visoke it was in itself a significant fact. If I could only find out more about the gorillas' apparent patchwork feeding habits in this strange forest I felt I would make even more exciting discoveries.

To my disappointment the nest site contained only seven nests. The tiny group appeared to be composed of one fully mature silverback, an almost mature blackback/silverback, two adults of unknown sex, two juveniles and a female with a small infant. I consoled myself, however, with the thought that a small family was at least a beginning, and far better than the fruitless days recently spent at Mukaba. After making a plan of the nest site we set off on the fresh trail.

I had not realized just how steep and hilly was this seemingly tiny area south of the road. Even the aerial photographs when viewed under the stereoscopic viewer belied the true steepness of the slopes. I realized that this was because many of them were obscured in tiny, dense, black patches in the photograph where the sun had failed to show the true relief on the shaded side of the steepest hills. Again and again we lost the trail and again and again the pygmies fanned out to find it once more. Finally among one enormous clump of shrubs which Patrice called 'Mhlere-Lhere' they lost it completely. My elation at finding a study group had now disappeared, to be replaced by the nagging fear that this area was also unsuitable for the sort of research I wished to do. We drove home in gloomy silence.

For some reason the trackers failed to turn up for work for a few days. When I discovered that they were complaining of much hard work and low pay I finally managed to woo them back with promises of a substantial increase in salary. This I discovered was quite justifiable for I had unknowingly been severely underpaying them. However, this meant I could now only afford to employ two of the four, so I chose Patrice and a younger man. As we drove to the Nyakalonge road Patrice began to sing and play a curious looking musical instrument, a 'likembe'. His accompanying song was lilting and haunting as he sang of days spent hunting in the forest. Suddenly he stopped playing and shouted 'Stop!' We got out to look at what his sharp eyes had spotted from the moving combie. 'Look at this,' he said, 'the gorillas have passed here.' Sure enough we found the same tell-tale signs of feeding on the herbs and vines at the roadside, and even a good knuckle-print in a patch of wet mud on the road itself. I placed my own knuckles into the depressions. The pygmies laughed at how tiny they were in comparison with the prints, which were each almost eight centimetres long and four centimetres wide, and tried their own even smaller hands.
 Nearby were clear signs that the gorillas had crossed the road that very morning. It seemed likely that this was the same group of seven animals. If so they were now heading back north to the region they had left a few days earlier. The only way to be certain was to follow the trail to the nest site and if possible get a sighting of the gorillas themselves and try and identify the silverback or another prominent group member. Only then could I be sure that I was consistently following the same group.
 I parked the kombie on a nearby slope and we set off to follow the fresh trail. We first had to scramble up an almost vertical bank at the side of the road and again I marvelled at how such large, and supposedly ungainly, animals had managed to negotiate such a climb. We had barely entered the forest when to my surprise it began to rain heavily. Usually the rains

came in the afternoon but today they were early. Fortunately, after an hour it was all over and the sun broke through again. Where it could penetrate the dense canopy it sent bright shafts streaming down like dozens of searchlight beams, which brought forth clouds of water vapour as the rain evaporated from the drenched leaves, and the air was soon humid and heavy.

We picked up the trail again and I kept hoping that we would not lose it as before. Today, however, there were several clear signs. Most significant of all were five lobes of dung which, from their size, obviously came from a large silverback gorilla. A little further on were peeled stems of 'Mushe' (*Urera hypselo-dendron*) and nearby some twigs from a large tree which Patrice called 'Bwamba' (*Myrianthus holstii*). Like 'Mushe', this tree, with its large, compound leaves very similar to a European horse-chestnut, figured frequently in the diet of the Kahuzi gorillas. That day the animals had eaten bark from the side branches and some of the leaves. I noticed, however, that only the tips of the leaves had been eaten and I tried to see how this had been done. After a little experimentation with some intact leaves which were still attached to the branches it became obvious. By sliding a cupped hand up from the leaf stalk the long spatula-shaped leaflets became folded together, so that the bunched tips could all be removed with one or two bites.

There seemed to be no apparent differences between the leaf tips and the rest of the leaf blade, each were rather tough and leathery. This was an interesting example of a high degree of selectivity in diet, for the gorillas could just as easily have eaten the entire leaf yet had consistently not done so. Was there a nutritional difference between the tips and the rest of the leaf blade? Or was it the result of the particular method of handling this compound leaf? Such questions were intriguing and could only be answered by carefully collecting a lot of data.

Just over two hundred metres away, to our complete surprise, we made a contact with the gorillas. Once more loud alarm barks and screams suddenly stopped us in our tracks. Once more we sat and waited but again I saw nothing save dense forest. After the initial vocalizations all was quiet for thirty minutes and sadly I realized that they had left. Frustration and weariness again replaced the feeling of excitement I had experienced on contact. Was this really going to take as long as both Adrien Deschryver and Dian Fossey had described? How could I study them, let alone habituate them, if I could not even see them or they me? Could it all be accomplished in the remaining twelve months before my research grant finished?

As I sat there again reflecting on the feasibility of the study I noticed a hole in the ground just ahead. 'What is this?' I asked Patrice. 'Chimpanzees,' he replied, 'they have eaten honey here.' Hardly able to believe my ears I went to examine the hole. The soil had been scraped aside to leave a funnel-shaped depression some forty centimetres across at the surface. It tapered to a narrow hole which was just large enough to enable me to put my hand down. By lying on the ground on my side I was able to reach the bottom of the hole with my outstretched fingers and thereby remove the few remaining scraps of the comb of a bees' nest. A few smaller remnants were scattered on the soil around the rim of the hole. The chimps had made a very thorough job of plundering the nest. But how had they managed to reach it? Lying nearby was the answer, which made me shake with excitement.

To a casual observer it would have been no more than a piece of twig broken from a nearby clump of *Alchornea hirtella.* Closer examination of it, however, revealed that its thicker end was frayed and the fibres were splayed outwards making it look like an old shaving brush. It had obviously been used by a chimp, or perhaps several chimps, as a digging stick! This untidy looking hole in the forest floor had been the result of an extremely intelligent piece of work, involving a faculty which, until recently, had been used to set man apart from his ape cousins – the use of tools. Jane Goodall had already exploded this myth with her observations of the termite-fishing behaviour of chimps at Gombe, using grass stalks as tools. Here now was an even more intriguing one, the use of a digging tool. Very carefully I measured, photographed and described the site in detail, much to the astonishment and amusement of Patrice. I wondered how the chimps managed to suffer the attacks of the angry bees, but this later became clear when I had them

identified by the British Museum, for they were stingless *Trigona*
species. On subsequent occasions when the pygmies gleefully
found such nests which had not yet been raided by chimps they
casually brushed off the swarming bees. With such selection
pressures as these I would not be surprised if stinging bees
evolved in the Kahuzi forests!

Excited by such a discovery, I tried to get Patrice to look for
even more evidence, but he declared that such finds were due
to luck and that systematic searches would be useless. Unfortunately I insisted that I wanted them to search and we argued
angrily about it. The next day the pygmies again did not
appear for work. I waited for almost an hour and then decided
to go and find their village and talk to Patrice. I discovered that
it was, indeed, a long walk from the main road. As I walked
further and further, I began to feel quite guilty about the
distances the trackers were having to cover each day – it was
truly 'much hard work'.

After half an hour I reached Patrice's village. It consisted of
a collection of half a dozen of the untidiest huts I ever saw in
Africa. They were taller than the huts used by the pygmies in
the forest, which I had seen in Colin Turnbull's photographs,
but were still a dome-shaped construction and completely unlike the mud-covered houses of the local Bashi peoples. Each
hut was covered with layers of leaves, though not a single hut
had a roof which looked secure or complete. Children of all
ages ran here and there, many of them completely naked or at
best with a tiny, filthy vest or shirt on the top half of their body.
Each one obviously had a heavy cold and constantly sniffed or
wiped a dribbling nose. Several goats chewed at nearby shrubs;
one was pulling leaves from the low roof of one of the huts.

Patrice and several other men were sitting near a blazing
fire, despite the fact that the sun was shining and the weather
was warm and clear. I gave my greetings and asked what the
problems were and why they had not turned up for work. Again
I was told of 'much hard work', and what was more, of my
unfair treatment of them the previous day. This I could not
deny for when I had cooled down I had realized how right
Patrice had been. Since the bees have no regular pattern in

where they build their nests a systematic search could take a very long time. I apologized for my behaviour and misunderstanding of the difficulties. I offered to employ two more trackers for a temporary period, whose sole job it would be to look for signs of chimpanzees, with the promise of a big reward for each sign of digging. Thus, honour and other difficulties duly satisfied, Patrice agreed to return to work and we walked together to the kombie. Once more the likembe played and again all was peace and happiness, and 'kazi mingi!' (much hard work).

At Nyakalonge we found the night nests surprisingly easily, only just over one thousand paces from the roadside. After 557 paces we had found four day nests where the animals had rested after their morning foraging. I was relieved to find seven night nests which indicated that this was still the same group which I had contacted almost a week earlier. Again, however, we lost the fresh trail and had to give up after several hours of fruitless searching.

On our way back to the kombie I heard loud screams accompanied by loud drumming in the distance. I looked enquiringly at Patrice. 'Chimps!' he exclaimed, 'close to the motor car.' We ran quickly down a natural trail which had no doubt been made some time in the past by elephants. At one point the trail went round the base of a huge tree. There I suddenly realized the cause of the drumming noises in the distance. The narrow trunk of this forest giant rose straight for some forty metres into the canopy. Since such a top-heavy structure could easily be blown over by the strong winds which frequently accompany the mountain storms, nature's architecture had coped brilliantly. The lower part of the tree was flared out into large, tapering buttresses which radiated from the trunk and gave a necessary stable base to support the huge crown high up in the canopy. I had read that chimpanzees in other areas would grip the edges of these flattened buttresses with their hands and then thump the sides with their feet and produce a deep, resonant drumming sound. Such trees were more typical of the lowland forest but obviously a few specimens had become adapted to the montane regions, or perhaps we were here in the upper limits of the 'transition forest' between lowland and montane regions. Although we ran quickly back to the roadside we only managed to catch a brief glimpse of the shadowy black figures of the chimps as they disappeared into the forest. Still it was more than I had seen of the Nyakalonge gorillas so far!

The next day was the start of the New Year, and turned out to be a spectacular beginning of a new era in my studies. Patrice had worked out an improved strategy for searching the area, so I was more optimistic. When we reached the forest the vegetation glistened from a recent downpour. As the temperature rose the air became more and more humid. Sweat rolled down my face, and my spectacles, constantly steaming up, were finally discarded. Soon, with the combined effects of sweat and rain-soaked vegetation, our clothes were thoroughly saturated. In an hour we reached a narrow valley which ran in a north-westerly direction for several kilometres. It contained several patches of open secondary forest and Patrice argued that the gorillas might come here to feed, and that if we walked along it we might meet them, or at least find their tracks.

Patrice was right; within ten minutes we had found tracks left by gorillas only the previous day. Rather than back-track to the nest site I decided to go on to find the nests vacated by the gorillas that morning. Then with luck I might also be able to make a contact. After a brief rest we started to follow the gorilla trail. Unfortunately it soon left the open valley and headed east.

Our progress was now very much slower, for Patrice had to cut a way through masses of dense vegetation. I suddenly realized that he was making the opening large for my benefit, for he and his companion could almost follow the tiny paths left by the gorillas. I urged him to make the trail as small as necessary and this made our progress faster though decidedly more uncomfortable. We crawled along like snakes and I realized we could have stumbled into one of the cobras or vipers which were common in this area. Fortunately they always cleared out of our way and I saw only three poisonous snakes during the entire study.

The trail suddenly came out into some bamboo forest and I feared we might lose it again but Patrice soon spotted some gorilla footprints on a muddy section and we were able to continue quite quickly. The gorillas had wandered in and out of the bamboo-forest interface and I wondered whether they were looking for remaining bamboo shoots. They had obviously not found any for there was not a single sign of feeding for over eight hundred paces among the bamboo. Then at the edge of the forest we found a Bwamba tree (*Myrianthus holstii*) at which the gorillas had fed on bark and leaves, again eating only the leaf tips.

We were now able to make faster progress in the more open vegetation and soon 1000, then 1400 paces showed up on my little counter. The trail now followed the top of the steepest ridge in the area and I was able to locate our position quite accurately on the aerial photograph. I had drawn a grid of one-centimetre-square quadrats over the photograph and on it I was plotting our route. The trail now headed down the steep east-facing slope through the bamboo. Again there were no young shoots to be found, all were now tall and mature.

At 1500 paces we found some *Hagenia* saplings from which the bark had been stripped and eaten by the gorillas. Only mature *Hagenias* had been present on Visoke and the gorillas had eaten slabs of its thick, corky bark. Would they have preferred the more tender bark from young saplings had it been present? What part did such unpalatable looking material play in the overall diet of the gorillas? As I was recording my observations it began to rain.

At first the rainfall was only light so we continued to follow the trail but after ten minutes the drizzle became a heavy downpour. However, I decided to keep on until we reached the nest site for at least then I would have that data to collect and examine until the rain stopped. I put on my waterproof coat and sou'wester. The pygmies had been wearing their hats all morning but I hated wearing mine for it closed around my ears and made me feel isolated from the forest sounds which were vital in tracking gorillas.

We plodded on down the slippery slope leaving the bamboo

forest behind, and eventually reached an area of denser mixed montane forest not far above the road itself. I checked the counter and made a note of the reading – 2000 paces. It was now well after midday and I wondered just how much further we would have to go to find the nest site. As I stepped forward to follow Patrice through the driving rain we were suddenly charged by a screaming silverback. The pygmies started to slap the bushes with their pangas. I murmured, 'No, no,' and out of habit I put Patrice and the other tracker down by my side and quickly sat down with them. The ground shook as the charging gorilla, now accompanied by another male, came screaming towards us. We were completely surrounded by dense bushes and I could barely see more than three or four metres ahead through tiny gaps among the leaves. Just when I thought the leading male would burst through the bushes and run straight into us, he stopped. I caught a glimpse of a huge face staring at us, then a flash of silver-grey as he turned away and circled above.

Before I could stop him the younger pygmy stood up and prepared to run away. Instantly both gorillas screamed and charged again. I pulled the youth down to the ground and the gorillas stopped just the other side of the nearest bush, barely two metres away. I gave several pacifying vocalizations, though by now my own heart was pounding so much that I felt unconvincing in my own performance. I muttered under my breath to the now terrified pygmy that if he ran away he would surely be attacked, but if he sat still, like Patrice, he would be safe. He did not say a word, but his eyes flashed back and forth in disbelief from me to the wall of vegetation all around us.

Loud crackling sounds floated eerily from above and to our right. Both animals were slowly and quietly circling around us. The tension proved too much and once more the young tracker stood up to try and spot them. Terrified, he pointed to a large female gorilla who was climbing into a nearby tree. She saw him and screamed loudly in alarm and fear before dropping to the ground again. The two males roared together and charged us from two different directions. Patrice raised his panga ready to defend himself. Fortunately, once more both males stopped within metres of colliding into us. I now had a firm hold on the would-be escapist and muttered vague threats to him in garbled Swahili as to what the gorillas, and I, would do to him if he ran! Eyes wide with fear he reluctantly sat down again to await his unknown fate. As another gorilla scream rang out from close by he was once more half on his feet but I quickly managed to push him down.

The rain slackened off and for the next forty minutes we were subjected to the most gruelling piece of intimidation imaginable. It consisted of slow, careful stalking in a circle around us, alternating with ear splitting vocalizations and ground thumping charges from the two males, always from two different directions. Each time they stopped only when it appeared to me they could see us through the nearby bushes. However, in the most recent charge the largest male seemed to be even closer before he finally stopped. The vocalizations were now sounding more and more frenzied above the returning downpour of rain.

I heard the two gorillas retreating towards the rest of their group higher up the path. Was this their final escape, or a way of getting a longer run for a further charge? I decided to slip away under cover of the noise of the rain and signalled Patrice and his now shaking companion to do so, but slowly. They needed no urging and crawled carefully and quietly for ten yards before breaking into a rapid helter-skelter down the wet slippery slope. Not wishing to be pounded as a martyr to their stupidity I ran after them, all thoughts of a silent escape now abandoned.

Loud screams and crashing vegetation announced that our departure had been detected, but by now it was too late, for all three of us were travelling like the mist and wind, falling and rolling down and down towards the road. In ten minutes of flight we reached the steep drop to the road and slithered thankfully down. Safe at last I roared with laughter and Patrice, old campaigner that he was, joined in. We both realized that the Nyakalonge gorillas, either from bluff or perhaps the start of a genuine attack, had made us run, and therefore lose face!

CHAPTER TWELVE

Kelele and his family

Ten days after my New Year's Day experience I had to start to habituate another primate to my presence. My daughter, Fiona, now almost two years old, arrived with Margaret. Unlike Mtoto, Fiona had forgotten me during our separation. It felt awful to be treated like a stranger by my own child when I went to meet her and Margaret at the airport. I decided to adopt the same tactics with her that I used with the gorillas, a slow, patient approach, while trying not to be too pressing for rapid success. It was equally frustrating with ape and human subjects alike for both ran to hide or to seek the protection of their mother at my approach. It took quite some time for them to settle down to life at IRSAC. Margaret had grown to love the peace and isolation of our tiny cabin on Mt Visoke and she now found the noisy, dusty main road running past our pavilion in the institute's grounds rather overpowering. I was lucky, for each day I could escape to my nearby forest world.

Unfortunately, while the Nyakalonge forests appeared to be an ideal study area on paper, they proved to be less so on the ground. We found it impossible to follow the same gorilla group on consecutive days owing to the difficulties of tracking in such a habitat. On each occasion that we contacted gorillas they responded violently and showed no signs of habituating to our presence. Considering the denseness of the vegetation it seemed unlikely that they would ever be able to see me sufficiently to realize that I had only peaceful intentions, for they usually let us get almost on top of them before they screamed and the male charged straight for us. I assumed that, like the Virunga gorillas, they would have sat quietly and let us pass by if possible, but the male would finally charge when we got too close.

Despite countless offers of huge *matabeeshis* for not losing the gorillas' trails and despite his superb tracking skills Patrice could not achieve the impossible. On several occasions we even followed the trail of other groups which had crossed that of my intended study group. This in itself was interesting but most confusing, since it was impossible to know which group we were following until I either counted the nests in a night nest site or heard the silverback of the group vocalize, for each sounded somewhat different. In over three months of study I collected masses of valuable data on gorilla behaviour and ecology, but unfortunately most of it was indirect evidence from trail signs, and my direct sightings of gorillas added up to less than one hour's total observation time! Twice I decided to leave Nyakalonge altogether. Each time I employed four more of Patrice's friends to help me find other gorillas in a more suitable area. We searched the forest on either side of the old road to Mukaba, and the forests bordering both sides of the great Musisi, but our efforts were rewarded by only very old trail signs of gorillas. Obviously these parts of the forest were used infrequently and then perhaps only as transit areas.

While trying to find a suitable area in which to study blue monkeys (*Cercopithecus mitis*), Hans Schlichte, another of the zoologists at IRSAC, had found recent signs of a large group of gorillas in the forest just north of the institute's farm at Tshibati. I immediately went to investigate and found a nest site of over twenty animals. Unfortunately this upset Michael Casimir, who now became worried that I was trying to move nearer to his 'territory'. I therefore returned to Nyakalonge determined to follow one group consistently. Again it proved impossible; the fluctuations in my nest counts indicated that there were three, possibly four, groups in the study area and we were still undoubtedly sometimes confusing the trails of different groups. I had learned a great deal from working in such difficult terrain, but how could I put such experience to its best use?

My chance came at the beginning of April, when Michael announced that he was going on safari for a whole month. Almost casually I asked him just before he left whether he minded if I followed one of the two partially habituated groups while he was away, the one, of course, which he was not studying himself. To my surprise he readily agreed, providing I gave him the ranging data when he returned. Elated at achieving my goal I switched study areas as soon as he left the main gate. Patrice and his latest companion, Atanazi, were both as delighted as I was at the change of plan. This was even more fortuitous for I discovered that much of the Tshibinda-Mbayo area we were now going into had once been Patrice's own hunting ground. Since each pygmy kept very much to his own area they therefore knew little about other parts of the forest. Patrice promised me that he would never again lose the trail of the gorillas. Before this area became a National Park he had already tracked many gorillas in this area for food. I had since learned from Adrien Deschryver that Patrice was the most skilful of all the hunters – and poachers!

While working in the west of the park it had become clear to me that the areas of secondary forest were very important to the gorillas. Not only did they provide abundant food in the form of bark, leaves, shoots and fruits, together with ample suitable nesting material, but it was all easily accessible to an animal which could walk along the ground, climb up trees, pull down vines and split open tough stems. The physique of the gorillas therefore was ideally suited to exploiting these resources fully, while their great stamina enabled them easily to cover the relatively short but strenuous journeys through the forest to find their food. But exactly how did they utilize a given area of forest? Natural selection would have favoured those animals feeding most efficiently and effectively on the available resources. Therefore, what form did the ensuing 'feeding strategy' of these gorillas take?

I was now confident that such questions could be answered in Kahuzi-Biega, if one could be sure of consistently following one or more groups on a day-to-day basis. With the help of Patrice and several of Adrien Deschryver's trackers I set out to find the missing group of partially habituated gorillas which Michael Casimir had decided not to study. I knew that it was unfair of me to 'poach' his territory but I also knew that his research was not questioning the aspects which I wished to investigate. I decided to gather as much useful data as possible before he returned from safari.

It was not as easy to find the group as I had imagined, but after one completely fruitless day, and another spent following what turned out to be a lone silverback who went for miles, we finally found a trail which was three days old. It led to a nest site containing twenty nests. I was overjoyed. At last I had found a suitable family! We followed the trail all day and eventually found the two subsequent nest sites and the fresh trail from that very day. We followed it as quickly as possible hoping to make a contact but it was already far too late in the afternoon. Although we were a long walk from where I had parked the car, Patrice explained that we could reach this spot very quickly the next morning by driving through the tea plantation and then walking over a nearby hill, which just happened to have one of Patrice's old poaching paths conveniently placed there! I agreed and returned to the laboratory at IRSAC to study the aerial photographs under the stereoviewer. As the hills stood out in three dimensions it was easy to follow where we had travelled that day and where Patrice intended to take us the next. His intimate knowledge of the terrain was already a tremendous help.

The following morning, much to the surprise of the girls picking the tea, we drove through the rough tracks leading through the plantation and parked the car near the border with the forest. Nearby were several shambas in a pocket of recently cleared forest which Adrien Deschryver had not been able to include in the park. Patrice led the way through a crop of maize. Most of the cobs had already been picked and some of the stubble burned. Soon the rest would be cleared and another crop planted. Suddenly Patrice stopped. 'Look at that, over there!' he exclaimed. I looked but could not see what he meant. 'What is it?' I asked. His face beamed. 'Ngila!' (gorillas). 'High, high in the trees over there.' I anxiously scanned the trees through my binoculars and there, over a hundred metres away and at least ten metres up in a tree near the edge of the forest, was a large black figure. It was a female gorilla. I scanned the vegetation near the female and soon spotted two more. I signalled the trackers to lie down and we tried to hide in the open stubble. However, the gorillas must have seen us, for they climbed down immediately and melted into the background vegetation.

I scanned each of the hundreds of 'black spots' in the forest hoping that each would prove to be a gorilla. Again Patrice was the first to spot a tiny movement as a juvenile climbed up a *Conopharyngia* tree. Patrice's eyes seemed not only to give him a normal wide angle view but also fantastic acuity which enabled him to pick out detail, and especially movement, over great distances. His talents seemed endless and he now became official 'spotter'. Unfortunately, however, not even he had eyes which could penetrate the dense secondary growth where rampant herbs and climbing vines almost completely covered shrubs and trees of all sizes. Instead of one or two layers of forest strata, here was an almost impenetrable continuous wall.

The juvenile was joined by another gorilla, an adult. They both sat motionless on a side branch and stared in our direction. It was impossible for us to hide in the open stubble so we kept still. I was lying flat with my binoculars resting on my rucksack. The animals were too far away to see any detail but we dared not move closer in case they fled. After looking at us for over five minutes they silently climbed down and disappeared from view. I waited for a further thirty minutes, then we crept forward and entered the forest. As we did so a loud alarm bark ended my hopes of another contact. The gorillas were now over a hundred metres away. Was I to follow them, cutting a way through this veritable jungle and thereby risk frightening them completely? Or was I going to be satisfied with that brief, tantalizing glimpse? Far from satisfied I had to be realistic and curb my impatience to see them, for the habituation of wild animals cannot be rushed and must take place gradually in order to gain their trust. I waited a further half-hour then set out to find their trail and trace their movements from the previous day.

We found the nest site, which the gorillas must have only just vacated, less than a hundred metres away. To my surprise and disappointment it contained only twelve nests. I was flabbergasted; had we again picked up a cross trail from another group and were we now following them? Patrice was as disappointed as myself and now, knowing the real difficulties of tracking in these forests, I could hardly blame him. We tried to think back to where we could have gone wrong, but the trail had led through masses of secondary growth and the flattened herbs and vines had been easy to follow. Thoroughly perplexed, we left the nest site to back-track and discover our mistake.

Eighty-three paces back along the gorilla trail we found the solution to our puzzle. The group had not slept together that night, but had split into two sub-units. Each sub-group contained the nest of a silverback but, most intriguing of all, I found not eight more nests as I expected, but ten. Some did not contain dung although they obviously had been slept in. Had two animals joined the group? Alternatively, did some animals start to nest with one sub-group and then later, possibly in the dark, move and sleep with the other sub-group? This latter explanation, however unlikely (for gorillas were not 'supposed' to move after dark), was in fact possible since I was later to observe animals, especially large infants and juveniles, building nests and then deserting them to build others somewhere else; but so, too, did animals leave and join groups.

It was a further two weeks before I made my first good observation of the gorillas in this group. Then I was able to see clearly how some of them fed on various plants, especially their staple item, 'Mushe'. I recorded the precise details of how each animal dealt with this and other food items so that I could later check to see if there were any differences between the feeding methods of age/sex classes, or indeed between individuals. I was able to see clearly that many of the leaves of 'Mushe', especially the younger ones, were not discarded but were actually eaten before the bark. Usually the feeding animal collected a whole bunch of leaves by pulling the long stem through its clenched fingers, then the whole bundle would be bitten or pushed into the cavernous mouth. Only when the animal started to concentrate on eating the bark were the leaves discarded, again being stripped from the stem in the same manner. The leafless stem was then either nibbled to pull off strips of the fibrous bark or, by the older more experienced animals, quickly pulled through clenched teeth thereby collecting the entire sheath of bark at one brief tug.

Thus my data on the daily lives of this group rapidly began to accumulate as earlier anomalies from trail data were clarified by direct observations. Soon Margaret was again busy typing up recorded data from one cassette while I was out collecting more. She worked extremely hard to interpret my whispered comments and keep my records up to date. Most of the contacts were either in the morning or near midday, but on the evening of 22 April I found the group just as they were building their nests at the head of an open valley next to the gravel quarry. I waited for over an hour in the dark, listening for any signs of movements or vocalizations. All was perfectly quiet and I finally crept away on tiptoe and returned to the car. Patrice and Atanazi had long since decided to walk the few kilometres down the road to their village. With fireflies lighting the trail while dancing their evening courtship displays all around me, I found the car and drove back to IRSAC to tell Margaret the good news.

After a hurried meal I grabbed my sleeping bag and returned to the forest. I was able to park my car in the quarry itself and as I turned off the lights and the engine I listened anxiously to see if I had disturbed the goliaths who were slumbering less than two hundred metres away. Only the humming chorus of the myriads of night insects could be heard. The day shift in the forest was long ended and all diurnal animals now slept soundly while the night shift took over.

I climbed quietly out of the car and absorbed the magical quality of the tropical rain forest at night. The nuptial dance of the fireflies was almost over and only a few who had failed to find partners still fluttered and flickered impatiently to and fro. Far in the distance below me I could see other lights flickering in the dark, but these were the man-made lights of the sprawling city of Bukavu thirty kilometres away, where over two hundred thousand people now lived. Nearby a lonely drum started to beat out a primitive rhythm and I wondered whether it was Patrice calling to the forest he loved so much, for it was certainly coming from his village. Although the nearby trees could have appeared menacing and frightening they now took on a different air as I learned to view them through Patrice's eyes. To the gorillas, too, they were, of course, home, and it seemed even more peaceful to imagine the twenty black figures fast asleep over the other side of the valley in the shelter of the tall trees. I was cowardly and shunned their shelter for myself but crept back into the car to curl up in my sleeping bag on the back seat. I slept fitfully as I waited impatiently for dawn to approach so that I could begin to observe the start of a long day in the life of the Kahuzi gorillas.

At a quarter past five I could bear the suspense no longer. I slid out of my sleeping bag, put on my boots and quietly crept to my chosen vantage point in the dark. All was quiet, even the insects of the night were waiting for the fast-approaching dawn. By five twenty-five it was getting appreciably lighter and ten minutes later I could read the dial of my watch without the aid of my shaded torch. At five thirty-seven precisely the first bird heralded the new day. I always found that the songs of the tropical birds were much shorter and more monotonous than the familiar and beautiful songs of the thrush or blackbird, but in the still morning air the simple two-note song of this woodland warbler sounded clear and beautiful, rather like a curlew. I had nicknamed it the 'gorilla bird' for it, or a closely related species, lives on Mt Visoke and I invariably heard it when I contacted the gorillas. Even when more and more birds joined in the dawn chorus and the day-flying insects added their shrill overtones, not a single gorilla stirred in its nest. In a little clear patch of the forest I could see a young adult lying in a nest built five or six metres above the ground on a tangled mass of vines. Nearby, among the topmost branches of a young, twelve-metre-high *Neoboutonia* tree, slept another young adult. A few metres below him was an enormous nest platform and the large black sleeping hulk occupying it could only belong to one of the largest females or a blackbacked male.

The first gorilla to greet the new day, one of the young adults, did so at seven minutes past six. Unfortunately, his dawn greeting came out of the wrong end of his alimentary canal and a

long, loud raspberry sounded rudely above the bird song! The
gorillas on Visoke had been similarly uninhibited and I attributed it to their huge intake of varied vegetable matter which,
on being decomposed by their gut flora, provided large amounts
of carbon dioxide and methane gas. The sharp grunting call,
'Ugh! Ugh! Ugh!', of *Cercopithecus mitis* rang out behind me. I
turned to try to locate the monkeys but they were too far away.
The forests sloped steeply down at this point and soon gave way
to plantation and shambas. Far away in the distance lay the
blue shimmering jewel of Lake Kivu backed by the dark sil-
houette of the rift valley mountains.

As I watched, a lip of gold appeared on the rim of the
mountains over in Rwanda and the sun climbed up above their
rugged peaks. Its rays flashed across Lake Kivu and bathed the
crowns of the forest trees in a warm, orange glow. I watched
fascinated, for as the sun rose behind me its rays crept lower
down the trees opposite until they touched the nests of the
sleeping gorillas, then finally reached the ground itself as the
sun emerged fully. Its rays were already warm and I had to take
off the quilted coat I had worn in the chilly night air. I scanned
the trees for signs of movement among the gorillas but in vain.
The blue monkeys started up their own dawn chorus. In comparison with that of the birds' song their harsh grunting was
ugly and menacing, just as I suppose it was meant to be, for no
doubt it was a territorial call signalling other groups to keep
away.

At six thirty the young adult at the top of the *Neoboutonia* tree
sat up, and to my surprise looked immediately in my direction.
It sat perfectly still like a miniature black Buddha. Ten minutes
later it came to life and in a leisurely way stretched its left arm
up into the air then lowered it again. A minute later it got up
and moving to the back of the nest it stuck its rump over the
edge. The bright rays of the sun lit up a stream of urine which
spattered down on to the vegetation below. The large adult
female below immediately sat up and watched as it fell past. I
wondered whether she thought it was rain! Still with its rump
over the rim of the nest the young adult then defaecated, sending large pieces of dung falling noisily into the vegetation below.

Here was a clear illustration of just how the Kahuzi gorillas kept their nests so clean. But why did they do so? Alternatively why did the Virunga gorillas defaecate *inside* their nests? From my observations so far I was certain that the Kahuzi gorillas did not produce any less dung per day than their Virunga counterparts, thus discounting Schaller's rather tenuous hypothesis.

Its morning toilet over the young adult went back to bed and lay down again, this time on its back. The large adult, too, lay down but on its stomach. As it did so another tiny black figure moved in the same nest. An infant was sleeping with its mother. A crackling of vegetation made me focus my binoculars on the mass of vines. I was just in time to see the other young adult climb down into the dense undergrowth. Just then there was more movement in the lower nest on the *Neoboutonia* tree and to my utter amazement a small juvenile climbed out. Three must have shared one nest! Just one minute later, at six fifty-five precisely, the huge female climbed out of the lower nest and was quickly followed by a small infant. She sat on a side branch, first urinated and then defaecated, and then, gripping the branch with both hands, she swung down below it and clambered down the main trunk. The infant did the same, though with much quicker, more nimble movements.

There were now many sounds of movement in the vegetation over the other side of the valley and other animals had obviously left their nests. Suddenly three of them, a large adult, a young adult and a juvenile climbed up into an *Albizzia* tree. I could see what they were making for – several large clumps of a semi-parasitic *Loranthus*, which seemed to be a highly favoured food item. The long sleep was now over, and huge empty stomachs were grumbling to be filled. The morning feeding session had begun.

But not for one young adult at the top of the *Neoboutonia* tree, for he lazily stretched his right arm out sideways and then rolled on to his side. Having a 'lie-in' no less! Meanwhile other hungry group members had climbed into the *Albizzia* tree and soon there were seven of them, including a huge blackbacked male, all feeding on *Loranthus* in the same tree. One large juvenile was over thirty metres above the ground. Unperturbed by the feeding on this obvious delicacy the lazy young adult slept on, occasionally stretching out one arm or both and once kicking his feet into the air. No doubt thoroughly enjoying his extended rest, he lay there until seven thirty-three, almost an hour longer than other group members. When he eventually got up he, too, paused on the large side branch but just sat there quite still. Perhaps he was thinking of the day ahead and whether to go back to bed. I chided myself for my anthropomorphic frivolity, but how else could one explain such seemingly human behaviour?

By going out of the quarry, which fortunately was not working that day, and walking down the nearby roadway I was able to get a little nearer to the seven gorillas feeding on the *Loranthus*. The highest of all, a juvenile, was hanging below one of the upper branches by his left arm, and both feet were pressed firmly against the main trunk. He reached outwards with his right hand and grabbed a single twig from a large ball of *Loranthus* which was hanging below the side branch. He then climbed back to a crotch in the tree and sat down to eat his prize in safety. He lifted the twig to his mouth and by twisting it round and round bit off many of the tiny, green-brown leaves. As though impatient with this rather laborious method he occasionally gripped one of the smaller twiglets between his thumb and forefinger and, with one smooth jerk, stripped off half a dozen leaves. These were then popped into his mouth with one hand while the other was twisting the stem to expose the remaining leaves. As he bit some of the leaves directly off the twigs even some of the stem was eaten, especially the thinner growing tips. From several stems he stripped off only the bark by gripping it between his incisor teeth and then tugging the twig away from his mouth.

When he had finished feeding on the twig he quite casually let it fall to the ground over thirty metres below. Then he stood up and gave a rapid 'diddle-diddle-diddle-dum' hand slap against the main trunk of the tree. This was a completely new form of 'chest-beat' to me and I could not decide whether it was given because I was nearby, or out of sheer joy after eating such a delicacy. He then turned and went back to collect some more

186

Loranthus, but this time the side branch started to bend and then broke sending him crashing through the vegetation, but as he did so he swung inwards on the breaking branch and managed to cling to the main trunk by wrapping both arms and legs right around its girth. His impetus carried him downward and, in a shower of falling leaves and displaced moss, he slithered like a fireman descending a pole. When he reached the next crotch in the tree he clambered over it and then slid down the next stage. So he descended until he reached the dense growth of vines clinging to the lower part of the tree trunk. As he disappeared amongst them I thought how lucky he was not to have fallen to the ground, but I was to see many more examples of the incredible climbing ability and general agility of the Kahuzi gorillas during the coming months. However, not all were so lucky for previous investigators of the skeletal remains of gorillas had shown over fifty per cent with at least some bone fractures.

The other six animals in the tree, apparently undisturbed by the near accident, carried on feeding on the other patches of *Loranthus*. There were two large adult females, three young adults and an enormous adult male who was almost a silverback. I nicknamed him Joe Brown after the famous English climber for he climbed so confidently. He was sitting on a side branch which looked barely able to support his huge bulk but he appeared to be too busy eating to concern himself with safety. Just then something moved violently in the corner of my field of view through the binoculars. I turned my attention on to a smaller *Neoboutonia* tree which was swaying violently. I soon saw the reason why. Climbing up it was the enormous silverback himself. I had decided to call him by a Swahili name, 'Kelele', which means 'noisy', for during each of the contacts I had had with him so far he had given a tremendous number of noisy vocalizations. Fortunately he never pressed home a charge. In fact, this was the first time I had seen him clearly, though he had been as close as two or three metres. Each time he had stopped when in dense vegetation nearby.

Today he, too, was climbing, and very expertly, though the tree swayed under his immense weight as he climbed higher. I could now see his goal. About twelve metres above the ground was a whole branch of *Loranthus* hanging from the *Neoboutonia* tree. Unlike the others this was covered in masses of red, honeysuckle-like flowers. He reached up with his right arm and pulled the two-metre-long branch down as though it were a mere twig, then he sat in the main fork about ten metres above the ground. The tree swayed gently to and fro as he moved. With the branch firmly across his lap he snapped off a small twig with his right hand then, lifting it up to his mouth, he bit off both leaves and flowers while twiddling the twig around until it was bare. Discarding that he collected another without flowers on it, this time with his left hand. While still holding it in his left hand he ran the fingers of his right hand up several twiglets stripping off all the leaves. These were then pushed in one bunch into his mouth.

Suddenly he flinched as a loud crack sounded near him, no doubt from a branch breaking under someone's weight. He stared in my direction and I realized that no matter how much I tried to hide or stay still each animal seemed to know exactly where I was located. When Kelele flinched he must have dropped the twig he was holding for he reached out and broke off another. It was larger and had bunches of bright red flowers. This time he gripped part of it inside his mouth and then, by tugging his hand away, he stripped off the terminal fifteen centimetres. As he sat there chewing leaves and flowers the end of the broken twig was sticking out of his mouth. It rolled from side to side between his lips. He looked most comical, rather like a general nervously chewing his cigar as he surveyed the battle scene. I chuckled as he flinched when another branch broke with a loud crack in the forest just behind him, for I imagined him swallowing and half choking on his 'cigar' in surprise. Instead I was surprised, for after he had chewed the leaves and flowers he casually swallowed the rest of the twig like a piece of spaghetti!

A movement in another nearby tree made me turn my attention from Kelele. I was just in time to see a juvenile climbing rapidly up into the upper branches of a *Dombeya goetzenii* tree. When it was near the top it walked out along a side branch and then from it transferred to another tree nearby. This was a much larger *Albizzia gummifera* and as the juvenile climbed higher and higher towards even more *Loranthus* I realized how intelligent he had been. The trunk of the *Albizzia* was far too large at its base to be encircled by his arms and there were no stems of strangling vines clinging to the trunk which would have provided suitable holds. So the juvenile had used the smaller more climbable *Dombeya* as a ladder to enable him to get to the smaller branches of the *Albizzia*. During the next hour several other gorillas followed his example. At one stage there was a 'passing point' situation as ascending animals waited patiently on one side branch while those descending climbed down via the other. While climbing down, one small juvenile carried a bare twig of *Loranthus* crossways in his mouth. Like a pirate carrying a cutlass descending the rigging of a ship, he scrambled down the tree. When still about twenty metres above the ground he dived on to a nearby mass of vines and disappeared among them, no doubt to do battle with his playmates using the home-made cutlass.

The group continued feeding, mainly on *Loranthus*, until 8.20 a.m., although some animals ate other food items such as *Urera hypselodendron*, *Taccaza floribunda*, *Basella alba* and *Helichrysum* sp. as well. Then one of the young males was the first to reach another of their favourite food items, a wild banana tree (*Ensete* sp.). I had already found many of these in my Nyakalonge study area which had literally been torn to pieces by the gorillas. They had eaten leaves, stem and the juicy pith as well as some fruit from the only tree I ever found bearing any. The fruit of the wild banana has a more speckled, orange skin than that of its cultivated counterpart (*Musa* sp.). In addition it is full of hard, black, marble-sized seeds. What little flesh there is available is so bitter that it dries out the lips and tongue immediately. Even Patrice, who would eat almost anything, had to force himself to suck the flesh from the seeds! From the many similarly treated seeds scattered beneath the pillaged banana trees it was clear that the gorillas however had enjoyed such bitter-tasting food.

There was no sign of any fruit on this wild banana but the

young male climbed up its stout stem and then settled himself down in the centre of the upper rosette of leaves, like the eye of a 'black-eyed Susan'. He grabbed hold of one enormous, two-metre-long leaf with both hands and pulled it towards him bending it over his lap. Then, closing his right hand around the leaf blade about thirty centimetres from its tip, he stripped the stout blade from the centre petiole with one smooth jerk. The handful of crumpled leaf blade was then eaten in three large bites. In this manner he stripped and ate almost half of the entire leaf blade before turning his attention to the thick petiole. With well-co-ordinated jerks of both hands and incisor teeth he quickly tore the outer green cortex away to expose the succulent white pith inside, which he then proceeded to eat in a long white strip as I would eat a stalk of celery.

A series of loud pig-grunts from the vegetation at the base of the wild banana announced the arrival of other group members. No doubt someone had got in someone else's way on the trail. As I stared at the ground cover, which was over a metre high, a large black arm appeared and pulled one of the banana leaves down to the ground. The leaf was then waved to and fro as it was folded back and forth. Soon the forest rang with tearing sounds and the entire tree shook as it was literally pulled apart by the feeding gorillas; other leaves were pulled quickly down and the tree became almost bare.

The vegetation at the base of the tree parted and there appeared a large silver-grey back; Kelele had arrived. He stood up almost bipedally and gripped one of the remaining leaf stalks just where it flared out from the main stem. With a mighty jerk he pulled the stalk clean from the trunk; this exposed large amounts of the central pith from the main trunk which Kelele proceeded to extract and eat. It was obviously very juicy for he frequently licked his lips as the sap squeezed out and ran over the whiskers on his jaws.

The group fed on this wild banana tree, and another one nearby, for a further forty minutes. Then the tearing sounds gradually faded away as more and more animals became satiated. By nine a.m. all was quiet. I was not able to see a single animal, yet I knew that each was resting not far away. At precisely 10 a.m., just when I was beginning to think they had after all crept silently away, Joe Brown climbed up into a *Neoboutonia* tree, fed on some *Loranthus* for twenty-five minutes, then climbed down again. His enormous pot belly could not have been satisfactorily filled in the first feeding session; presumably now satisfied, he climbed down once more to rest.

Soon the other sounds of the forest from countless insects, birds and the occasional blue monkey filled my ears while the gorillas rested for a further forty minutes. Then I heard a brief outbreak of 'pig-grunting' which turned into screams as several animals chased each other round and round, hidden by the forest. After thirty seconds the screams died down but from one animal they turned into a pathetic whimper. It was so infuriating not to be able to see what was going on! Finally the whimpering, too, died down and I could hear that the group were on the move away from me. Soon even these faint sounds had disappeared and the gorillas had gone.

Patrice and Atanazi had walked up from their village and were waiting at the side of the road. I signalled to them to come over to where I was. As I wanted to circle round and join the gorillas again I asked Patrice which would be the best way to go. He led the way down the road and through the tea plantation. Soon we were heading back into the forest along another trail. Suddenly Patrice, who was leading, ran helter-skelter through the forest away from us as though pursued by some demon. I did not hear what he had shouted before he took off and I just stood there gazing after him as he ran with a peculiar motion, his knees jerking higher and higher as he seemed to skip through the forest. A sharp pain in my leg made me look down. There was the reason for Patrice's strange behaviour: we were standing among a moving column of safari ants! I rushed after Patrice with Atanazi close on my heels. Truly we must have been a comical sight as we, too, copied Patrice's skipping gait, slapping the biting hordes of safari ants as we ran.

I caught up with Patrice just as he was about to cut his way through a dense bush. His panga flashed downwards in a wild flailing motion as he hacked at the vegetation. 'Whaugh-augh-augh-augh-augh!' A great scream of rage and alarm stopped us dead in our tracks and made us forget even the needle-sharp bites of the safari ants. We had run straight into Kelele! There was no alternative but to retreat back through the safari ants. They were now swarming right over the trail and had covered a nearby wild banana tree. The column must have spread out far and wide for we had to run for ages before we were free of them. Then we had even more hilarious scenes as we each tried to shake off the ants still clinging to our clothes. We even had to strip off our trousers and turn them inside out and carefully extract each elusive would-be biter. Some had also got into our hair, no doubt falling on us as we rushed through the vegetation, so we had to stand in line and mutually groom each other to remove them. Fortunately Kelele did not pursue his advantage to catch the trouserless trio and we were left in peace to rid ourselves of ants, and laugh uproariously at what had happened.

After putting on his trousers again Patrice yelled a Mashi curse, slapped his own backside and took his trousers off again to search for the elusive miscreant. This was to happen to all of us many times, for the ants seemed to be able to get right into the overlapping seams of the material and only emerged to bite when we had put our clothes back on. Chiding Patrice for his 'wonderful trail', we returned to the tea plantation. Not to be outdone Patrice led us via another trail, mercifully without safari ants, and eventually we could hear the gorillas foraging. Soon we heard the familiar sounds of yet another wild banana being torn apart. Patrice looked at me and laughed. 'They are eating the banana tree with the safari ants!' he said. So it must have been, for we had circled around the group without finding any other *Ensete*. I later found other examples of the gorillas walking seemingly unhurt through safari ants: presumably their hair is too coarse for the ants to penetrate. If the gorillas were eating the leaves they must also be eating the ants, since they were all over the foliage, but I put it down to incidental eating of animal matter! I would dearly have loved to be able to see what was happening, but we dared not risk annoying Kelele further.

The gorillas fed on the wild banana and foraged along slowly in the nearby vegetation until almost two p.m., then once again the noises of feeding began to diminish – so much for Adrien's theory of a twelve to two rest break! So far the group had only moved approximately three hundred metres from their night nests which, in a direct line, could only have been two hundred metres away. At that point the smallest of the three males I had so far seen in the group popped his head out of some vines ten metres above the ground some fifty metres away. He stared directly at me: once again I had been discovered. Another black shadowy figure appeared at his side and he moved out of the way. One of the large females then pushed her way right out into the open and stood quadrupedally on top of the vines. She, too, stared straight at me, but after thirty seconds she turned and sat down with her back towards me. Then she reached out with both hands and began to pull a lot of the vine stems in towards her. She pushed these down in front of her and then turned to her left. As she did so I caught a glimpse of an infant just behind her going through exactly the same motions – a lesson in nest building. The female continued to pull vines in towards her while she rotated in a squatting position treading the vegetation down with her feet. Finally after only two minutes' work she sat down in her completed day nest facing me. Nearby her infant was still fiddling with some small vines at the edge of his nest. He, too, was finally satisfied and sat still, but only for a minute and then he began to pull in more and more vines. One day he would build his nest completely apart from his mother, probably by the time he was three and his mother's next infant was born.

It began to drizzle. Both animals sat there staring blankly at me while I put on my waterproofs. They did not even vocalize or move when I slowly put up my tiny green umbrella. It rained gently for over half an hour then the rain turned into a fine mist before finally ceasing altogether, but by this time the air and the vegetation were so saturated that it hardly made any difference when the rain stopped. Most of the animals were obviously resting and digesting their huge intake of food, but occasionally I heard the unmistakable sounds of infants play-wrestling as they expended their excess energy. The first signs of movement came at three thirty when one of the branches in a

Myrianthus tree began to shake violently. Ten minutes later a loud chest-beat rang out followed by the 'wha-wha-wha-wha!' screams of females having another argument. This quickly subsided and I could hear the group moving further and further away. By ten minutes past four they were a hundred metres away and out of earshot. I looked at Patrice, who instantly read my thoughts. 'They are going over there, near the tea plantation.' We quietly retreated and, returning to the boundary of the forest and the tea plantation, began to creep along the edges of the forest.

It took us less than ten minutes to find them again. As usual Patrice was the first to see them. He attracted my attention by sucking air gently through his teeth, then with a broad grin on his face, he nodded his curly head towards the forest on our left. There was a tiny infant hanging by one hand from a branch about five metres above the ground. As we watched it slowly turned around like a tiny, black pendulum. Just then a female climbed up into the same tree and the infant jerked himself sideways. Reaching out with his free hand he touched her then swung back. The female sat down on a branch below the infant and then reached up with both hands to push at the swinging infant pendulum. He grabbed hold of one of her arms and climbed down it to sit at her side on the branch. His mother quickly turned and with mouth open wide she nibbled the top of his head in a mock attack. For the next ten minutes we were treated to a beautifully moving display of mutual teasing by mother and infant which even had the pygmies chuckling inwardly with mirth. How could Patrice and Atanazi still think of the gorillas merely as potential food, after seeing them playing like their own children? I thought. I was glad that they, too, were able to see this gentle side of the gorillas' family life. No doubt the rest of the village would also share the experience around the camp fire that night. Perhaps they, too, would view gorillas differently in future.

The group continued to move along slowly, with each animal stopping here and there to feed from some choice collection of herbs or vines. At ten to five I heard the deep rumbling of thunder rolling over the distant slopes of Mt Kahuzi. Five

minutes later I saw the first of the group, a juvenile, build his
night nest almost twenty metres up in a *Neoboutonia* tree. The
tree swayed about as he pulled in branch after branch; folding
them down towards him he trod them in with his feet while
slowly turning in a circle, just as the female had done. Then,
with a brilliant feat of architectural ingenuity, he solved his
stability problem by incorporating the tips of several branches
from a nearby tree into his nest. He then lay down on his back
but continued to feed on the leaves of some nearby 'Mushe' –
supper in bed!

Over the next hour I watched as one after another all members of the group gradually stopped feeding and built their own
night nests. One juvenile had just completed an elaborate nest
in a *Conopharyngia* tree, which had taken him almost fifteen
minutes to make comfortable, when a large female and her
infant, the same two I had just observed playing together,
appeared at his side. As they sat down he got out of his nest and
moving to one side, began to construct another adjoining nest.
The female and her infant then occupied the vacated nest. So
that was how it was done! I wondered if the obliging juvenile
was a previous offspring of the female? He was certainly about
the right age for this to be possible.

Two other young adults did not start to build their nests until
twelve minutes past six, almost eighty minutes after the first.
They, too, built their nests among the matted vines growing on
the same *Conopharyngia* tree as the juvenile and the mother with
her infant. Unlike the others they built their nests in less than
a minute, in fact one merely pushed his way into a clump of
vines and then lay down on his back – yet another reason for
getting false 'nest' counts. I therefore knew the exact position
of seven animals; a small juvenile, a large juvenile, a large
female with a medium sized infant, and three young adults, and
all were nesting above the ground.

By now it was quite dark and the fireflies came out for their
evening dance as the thunder rumbled again and again around
Mt Kahuzi and then came nearer following on the heels of the
mist and rain. I waited until all was quiet at the nest site then
slowly crept away to leave the gorillas to sleep in peace, and

most probably in rain. I had been incredibly lucky to observe so much of their natural behaviour. I could hardly wait for the next day in the life of my new study animals to begin.

After sharing such a unique experience with Kelele's family I knew that I could not now abandon them on Casimir's return. There was obviously ample work to keep several researchers busy, but how was I to convince Casimir of this? I reasoned that if we were to try and fully understand the behaviour and ecology of any gorillas, especially the Kahuzi ones to see how different they were from other populations, then it was vital to have accurate data on all the possible influences on their daily life.

Obviously a factor of major importance could be the presence and influence of neighbouring groups. No one had ever before studied two neighbouring family groups simultaneously. So when Casimir finally returned from safari I hopefully suggested to him that we conducted such a study together. To my complete surprise and sheer delight he immediately agreed. I rushed back to our apartment to tell Margaret the good news. To celebrate she made a special dinner and we opened a bottle of wine and drank a toast to my newfound family. (A family composed of one silverback male (Kelele), one blackback/silverback male (Joe Brown), three blackbacked males, four adult females, three sub-adults (of unknown sexes), two juveniles, five infants and a 'peripheral' silverback male.)

CHAPTER THIRTEEN

Treed by gorillas

Adrien Deschryver was also pleased that I had been able to come to an amicable agreement with Michael Casimir, for this meant that both of the partially habituated gorilla groups would now be studied. However, I was subject to the same agreement he had with Michael, that if any tourists arrived to see the gorillas they would be allowed to do so: it was understood that tourism took priority over scientific research. Since the park itself had been especially created for this purpose, and it now desperately needed both the income and international publicity which tourists would bring, this was quite natural. Unfortunately, only a very few had so far visited the park, but this was to change and at the end of April 1972 the first major influx arrived in the form of no less than a Hollywood film crew!

Adrien decided that since my group was in the most accessible area, near the meteorological station on Mt Bukulumisa, it would be easy for the film crew to set up camp on a site he had there and follow the group for a week. Fortunately he let me join them so that I could continue my own study. The crew consisted of only four people. The director explained that the footage they would shoot on gorillas would be just a small part of a full length feature film of the *2001 Space Odyssey* type. Full of the brash confidence that presumably only Hollywood can give he grandly described how he had read all about the gorilla and was going to show in the film 'this pathetic side-shoot of the primate evolutionary line'.

I tried to point out that there was a lot of good scientific evidence which painted a very different picture of the gorilla. I suggested that a wonderful film could be made of the truly remarkable adaptability of the gorillas to their particular habitat. Such a film would serve the dual purpose of showing people some of the wonders of animals and their evolution and the desperate need to save such animals from extinction. However, I felt that my comments fell on ears already deafened by a fixed plot. How could a 'poor miserable failure of evolution' be recast as the hero of a success story? The script had obviously been written and the gorilla's role already clearly defined for him.

However, the gorillas, the forests and the elements did not accept their type-cast role so easily. After a frustrating day spent toiling through rain-soaked forest, carrying heavy cameras up and down steep hills, we finally found the gorillas climbing in dense vegetation where the light was too poor for filming. More rain further dampened already low spirits and expensive cameras alike. The next day the director announced that he had to fly to Kigali on urgent business and would therefore leave the filming to his cameraman. Luckily the cameraman, Helmut Barth, was made of much sterner stuff, a real professional nature photographer who had already shot many films of rare animals. He told me that he had dreamed for years of making a film of gorillas in their natural habitat. Now that he was here at last he would struggle through any difficulties the forest could offer until he had the opportunity to film. Unfortunately he would not have any say in how the footage would finally be edited, for it would go directly to Hollywood.

Helmut carried his own enormous Arriflex camera carefully cradled in his arms as we trudged through swamps, along valleys and over hills. As soon as we made a contact he would quickly and hopefully set it up on its tripod and then search the forest for the elusive black apes. He never once grumbled despite several days of frustration and very little useful film to show for all his hard work. He told us how he had often spent weeks waiting for rare animals to visit waterholes or known courtship areas. On some occasions when the animal finally arrived it was too dark for filming, but on others his patience was rewarded with the opportunity to film rarely-seen events. Such an opportunity was all he asked for now, and he did not care how far he had to carry his camera to find it.

Working in such conditions will either bring people together or push them further apart quite quickly. In just a few days Adrien, Helmut and I found that we had a great deal in common and we got on very well together. The budget for the film only allowed them just over a week's stay in Kahuzi so I hoped that Helmut at least would get some good footage. Not surprisingly the gorillas seemed much more nervous than usual and we could not get close enough for good prolonged observations. However, Helmut's chance finally came when we found the group feeding over the other side of a narrow valley. With the aid of huge telephoto lenses (one was a metre long) he was at last able to film in good lighting conditions for almost an hour. His voice was filled with excitement as he asked for further film magazines to be passed to him. His eyes sparkled and his face beamed with delight as he filmed. I knew exactly how he felt. The aches and pains of the day's tracking are forgotten when such a contact is made. Then you record your observations as rapidly as you can to illustrate the burst of activity you can see at last. Suddenly it is all over and they have melted into the forest again leaving you only with your memories. Today, however, those memories had been captured on film and could be relived not only by ourselves but by millions of people all over the world. I was pleased that Helmut had succeeded in making his dreams become reality.

The crew stayed for a few more days but only managed to get one more good opportunity to film. They were subjected to a fine display charge from Kelele, who almost bowled over the director and his camera in dense vegetation. Fortunately as usual he stopped at the crucial moment. I wondered whether in the coming months the director would still have the same opinion of gorillas as he had when he arrived in Kahuzi. As he relived those moments over and over again, recalling the terrifying charge right up to the moment he thought he would be killed by the gorilla, would he still wish to portray it as a pathetic creature?

Helmut was genuinely sorry to be leaving and he and I discussed the possibility of making a scientific film of the true daily life of the Kahuzi gorillas. Adrien was in agreement if the

park could have a copy of the film for its own publicity purposes. We finally parted company, each with something to look
forward to for the future – I with sharing the daily life of the
gorillas with other people, Helmut with the possibility of making
a beautiful film, and Adrien with the hopes that more and more
people would then come to see the gorillas and the park for
themselves and take an interest in its preservation.

My study group had been hard pressed by the film crew for
over a week. I began to fear that Adrien, in his enthusiasm to
get Helmut in a suitable position to film the gorillas, had pushed
them too hard. On some days we had made further contacts
if the initial one was unproductive for photography. Again
Adrien was going against the habituation procedures of 'do not
follow', which Schaller had shown to be so successful. By
pushing the group too relentlessly not only could it influence
their habituation to us, but I recalled the plight of the two
Japanese scientists, Kawai and Mizuhara, who had insisted
that their guide should continue to follow a gorilla group on
Mt Muhavura after their initial contact. The silverback reacted
violently and charged downhill towards them; he did not stop
but ran straight at them, bowling over the guide and both
scientists. Fortunately, although badly shaken, all were safe,
but they could so easily have been injured either by a blow
from a mighty, flailing forearm or from a bite given as the
gorilla charged past, both tactics which gorillas use on each
other. Despite several close calls the Hollywood film crew were
now safely on their way out of the country, but I had to face
the group again the next day and try to restore their trust.

The morning of 9 May was dark and overcast and I drove
up the narrow winding roadway to Mt Bukulumisa full of
apprehension. This feeling increased when we discovered that
the group had left the area below the meteorological station and
headed north-west. As I followed the trail my fears that we
had in fact pressed the group too hard and they were now in
flight seemed to be confirmed, for their trail led in a line so
straight that surely only panic could be the cause of such a
change in the pattern of their movements. This was further

supported by the trail signs which showed that the group had obviously travelled in single file without pausing to feed on the way.

As usual I was recording the number of paces between successive nest sites. Just as I clicked up 1600 paces on my counter we reached the edge of a large swamp. I examined the aerial photograph and was able to pinpoint our locality exactly. This was a narrow swamp which ran north to south parallel with part of the great Musisi, south of the main road. We were near its northern tip and I could make out the secondary forest which bordered the road less than a kilometre away. Once again I was thankful for those wonderfully clear pictures, without which I could easily have mistaken my location.

The gorillas' tracks led along the side of the swamp for almost two hundred paces and then turned directly into the swamp itself. The group had left a clear trail where they had flattened the tall *Cyperus* reeds as they zig-zagged across. There was no danger of sinking in such a swamp for the sub-stratum, although sometimes ankle-deep in water, consisted of firm humus. It looked as though the gorillas had pushed the flat reeds down in front of them thereby forming a drier platform on which to walk. This was rather difficult for bipedal creatures like ourselves to do, so we had to put up with the freezing cold water which poured into our boots.

Patrice was in the lead as usual, I was following immediately behind him and Atanazi brought up the rear. As we plodded on I began to get suspicious about the trail for I noticed some dung which did not appear to be from the previous day. Although quite cold to the touch this could just as easily have been due to the influence of the swamp water as the cold night air. I showed it to Patrice and questioned him about the trail. 'Is it today's?' I asked. He was adamant that this was not so. 'It is only yesterday's. We have not yet seen the nests,' he said pointedly.

Where tracking was concerned I was by now content to let Patrice be the 'Bwana mkubwa' (big boss), so we pressed on. However, I began to feel uneasy again when I saw further pieces of quite fresh looking dung. The *Cyperus* reeds all around us were over head height and we could not see more than a few metres ahead. In such a situation we could easily have stumbled right into the gorillas before we or they realized it. Thus it was vital to know whether the trail was of yesterday, in which case we could proceed with due speed and less caution, or today, which could mean trouble if we were careless. I questioned Patrice again. '*Is* it today's?' He seemed rather cross as he impatiently replied, 'No, it is only yesterday's.'

We pressed on for another 130 paces. I spotted some more dung and went in front of Patrice to examine it for myself. It was warm! I was just about to tell Patrice to feel the dung for himself when we heard a loud 'pop, pop, pop, pop, pop' just ahead of us. I had already heard such sounds before, they were the sounds of *Cyperus* reeds being pulled up by gorillas so that they could eat the juicy basal portion. Patrice looked at me and his face lit up with a smile of amusement, disbelief and trepidation. 'It *is* today's!' he announced rather belatedly, 'but where are the nests?' At that moment the loss of the nests was a minor problem and I could cheerfully have sent Patrice forward towards the gorillas by himself just to check that they were really there! We had to retreat carefully, slowly and as quietly as possible. With each crackle of brittle stems and splash of misplaced feet I expected to hear Kelele's roar and then hear him pounding towards us. However, we managed to get out of earshot without causing any such repercussions and headed for the nearest area of forest.

Patrice was quite amused at the whole business and I ribbed him for his mistake saying that it could easily have resulted in a fatal charge. To Atanazi's amusement I told Patrice that if he made a similar mistake in the future and Kelele charged I would push him down in his path while Atanazi and I made our escape. Not to be outdone, Patrice demonstrated with his panga how he would reduce Kelele to several pieces of gorilla steaks and then eat him!

I was now faced with a problem. Did I go back to find where the gorillas had nested for the night or did I try to stay near the group? It was only nine fifteen so the group could still be feeding in the swamp. It would be impossible to make a contact in such conditions so I looked around for a vantage point on the nearby hill which would enable me to look down into the swamp. The hill was densely covered with swamp forest which seemed unlikely to offer open views. Then I noticed a large branch sticking out horizontally from one of the trees on the hillside and overhanging the swamp. If I could get up there I might be able to see the gorillas. I therefore told Patrice and Atanazi to back-track and find the night nests while I tried to observe the group.

Quietly we went our separate ways, they back through the swamp and I into the edge of the dark forest. I eventually found the correct tree and, leaving my rucksack at its base, I straddled the trunk and pulled myself upwards and outwards over the swamp. I scanned the vast stretch of *Cyperus* with my binoculars but was disappointed to find that although I was now some seven metres above the swamp I still could not see the gorillas.

Suddenly a small jet-black figure appeared above the golden-green of the reeds about eighty metres away. A small juvenile was climbing a young *Hypericum* sapling which was one of several growing in a drier part of the swamp. As the juvenile climbed above the tips of the reeds the sapling started to bend and he fell down. I scanned the vegetation around the clump of *Hypericum* saplings and could discern occasional movements among the *Cyperus* reeds. One was pulled up with a 'pop' which rang clearly over the swamp. I watched it as it waved about and then disappeared but I could not see the animal which was feeding.

It seemed likely that most of the group were now resting in this drier patch of the swamp, something which I had already recorded a few weeks earlier. It looked as though I could be in for a long boring wait in my tree so I made myself as comfortable as possible. A few minutes later, however, I was surprised to hear some branches being broken in the tree-covered hillside not far from the group. These were followed by two more loud cracks, then a chest-beat followed by another branch break. The group had obviously split; some had gone into the forest while the remainder were resting in the swamp. There was a strong wind blowing across the swamp behind me and I began to wonder whether it was carrying my scent to them. At that moment there was a lot of movement at the borders of the forest and the swamp, and it seemed likely that other group members were now leaving the swamp for the forest. A few minutes later I could hear the sounds of a great deal of movement among the reeds. The rest of the group were on the move, and were heading straight for me.

I could hear them getting closer and closer, but still could not see them. I could only hear their gentle growls and see the waving reeds which marked their progress towards me. They got to within forty metres before I caught glimpses of black figures passing between gaps in the trampled reeds. Some animals had spread out to feed on the *Cyperus* and the air was filled with the 'pop, pop, pop' as the reeds were pulled up. As they got nearer I could hear 'throat-clearing' vocalizations among the growling which was now more intense. It was as if a crowd of youngsters were approaching in the distance and all I could hear was the babble of their conversation without actually being able to understand a single clear word.

A small juvenile appeared briefly about twenty metres away then turned and vanished among the reeds again. At that moment I heard the sound I was dreading, the chattering voices of Patrice and Atanazi returning from the nest site. I looked behind me and could clearly see them picking their way carefully through the reeds. I waved to them to stop, but they were so busy chattering that they did not see my frantic signal. I had tried hard to get them out of the habit of talking while we were tracking but it was no use, it was such a part of their lives that they obviously found it impossible to change their habits. In a way it filled the forest with more life but at such a moment as this it was likely to fill it with imminent danger.

I looked back towards the approaching gorillas and was just in time to catch the first glimpse of the silverback. He was slowly walking forward in the familiar 'knuckle walking' gait, and as he walked he moved his head from side to side with his nose high in the air. He seemed to be testing the air and I wondered if he had in fact detected my scent, quite a considerable one for I had been sweating profusely from our march.

The situation was now desperate for I could still hear the pygmies clearly behind me. The silverback kept on slowly plodding
forward and it seemed likely that the dense reeds around him
were shielding him from the sounds. Being well above their
muffling effect I could hear both sets of approaching primates
quite clearly.

The silverback was being closely followed by five other
animals all crowded close behind him as though vying with
each other to be closest to him. They were now only ten metres
away and were walking directly towards my tree. I thought
that at any moment one would look up, see me, and scream in
fear. Or they might hear the pygmies and rush into the forest,
then see me and feel that they were threatened on both sides.
There was no other alternative: I announced my presence to
them with a gentle though very self-conscious 'Come, come,
come, come!'

Kelele gave an 'Uh-uh-u?' questioning bark and sat down.
He looked up at me sitting in the tree and his mouth was still
slightly open. I had obviously caught him completely off guard,
for his expression was most comical as if to say, 'What on earth
are *you* doing up there?' He sat leaning back and stared up at
me while two small infants clambered over other animals and
climbed up into two small *Hypericum* saplings growing on either
side of their trail. Four other group members sat down behind
and to the side of Kelele and it made a beautiful family picture,
but my camera was resting at the bottom of the tree.

The peaceful domestic scene was suddenly and rudely shattered by the younger male, Joe Brown. Pushing his way forward
he got into a position just behind Kelele and looked around for
the source of the hold-up. When he saw me he screamed loudly
and immediately rushed off out of the open swamp and into the
nearby dense forest. Kelele then got up, gave a 'wraugh' of
threat, beat his chest and rushed off after Joe Brown with the
rest of the group tumbling after him. To try and quell the
obvious panic I gave some more gentle vocalizations, but
another male reached the spot vacated by Kelele, saw me and
added his own high-pitched 'wraugh' of threat, then he, too,
rushed for the forest. Kelele added his much deeper threat bark

in an echoing reply.

Within seconds all the group had disappeared into the dense primary vegetation on the hillside just in front of me. I could hear the leaves rustling as they passed through. Then another questioning bark rang out, 'Uh-uh-u?' This was followed immediately by threat barks, screams and chest-beats in a pandemonium of panic responses. I added a feeble 'come, come, come' and a few hopeful 'baby-like' vocalizations. The forest became absolutely quiet, then I heard the faintest of rustles in the dense vegetation immediately above me. They had circled around me. Just then a branch broke with a loud crack in the forest nearby. Immediately the whole group erupted in vocalizations, the males roared in chorus and I could discern three different levels of pitch, presumably because of their differing sizes and stages of maturity. The deepest was obviously Kelele's while that of the youngest male verged on a scream. Unlike the other two he kept vocalizing as all three suddenly charged downhill towards me.

The vegetation was so dense that I still could not see a thing, not even the base of the tree I was sitting in. But the actions of the males did not need to be seen to be understood and I could well imagine what they looked like as I heard their pounding feet getting closer. They stopped by a smaller tree a few metres from the base of the one I was perched in and, in a show of either intimidation or just sheer strength, one of them shook the trunk as though it were a reed from the swamp below. I looked down at the swamp and, half expecting to be shaken from my seat and fall like a ripe fruit into the quagmire, I clung more tightly to my own precious tree trunk and wondered what I could do next. Again they screamed and then charged once more, this time to the foot of the tree I was in.

I cursed the denseness of the vegetation which was preventing the gorillas from seeing me. I was afraid that one of them might get over-excited and charge straight up the inclined trunk of my tree and suddenly burst out of the branches on top of me. Seeing me suddenly so close he might then panic and either he or I, or both, could end up in the swamp below – perhaps the most acceptable of various alternatives! I had no choice but to resort to my ultimate deterrent. Although I knew that its use could instantaneously end my habituation programme and with it my study of this family, I drew my pistol from my pocket. Pointing it at arm's length towards the spot where I expected to see a screaming gorilla at any second I curled my finger around the trigger and waited, hardly daring to breathe.

The forest was again eerily quiet. It was like being in a dream world of complete unreality, where time stood still and everything was dead but was about to spring into vociferous life again at any second. I was not afraid for myself, because I still refused to believe that the gorillas would attack unless they accidentally ran into me, and here the vegetation was the crucial factor. I was afraid for them. Would I shoot if they got too close? Could I shoot? What good, or more likely, what harm, would it do? Was this the result of pressing the group too hard? In these timeless moments unanswerable questions flashed through my mind as I waited for the gorillas to decide the outcome of our strange situation.

Some leaves crackled nearby and I slowly turned my head to see what was happening. A large female gorilla was climbing into a nearby tree and close behind her was another. With a huge sigh of relief I slowly put my pistol in my pocket out of sight. After my unfortunate experiences on Mt Visoke I now carried only a tiny starting pistol, the sound of which, in the muffling influence of the forest, was reduced to a mere 'pop', and I doubted its effectiveness in such circumstances.

The crisis had obviously passed for the females would not climb near me if the males were waiting to charge again. Or would they? I began to wonder as both females sat down in the fork of a tree only five metres away and stared intently at me. Perhaps they wanted ringside seats for the grand finale which the males were now about to perform! My doubts were soon removed as one of them turned away and nonchalantly began to feed on some epiphytic ferns hanging beneath one of the branches. I was now excited and happy to think that they still trusted me so much, but not so Patrice, for he told me later that when he and Atanazi first heard the screams they hid in the swamp. They could clearly see me sitting on the branch and followed the subsequent events with great anxiety. I had to hide my amusement when Patrice solemnly said that when they saw the two large females climbing up the tree, both he and Atanazi prayed for me, for they thought the gorillas were coming to get me.

They need not have worried for the females showed neither fear nor aggression as they watched me, just curiosity which gave way to disinterest as they turned to a more important topic – feeding. One of them climbed even higher until she was almost directly above my head, then, leaning right over the branch, she began to collect more epiphytic ferns daintily one by one and finally popped the whole handful into her mouth. For no apparent reason the female still sitting in the fork of the tree opposite me slapped the main trunk five times with the palm of her right hand. Gentle throat-clearing noises and growls floated up from the base of my tree followed by the reassuring sounds of teeth tearing the bark from tough stems or chewing succulent leaves. As I tried to pierce the forest gloom below, two more black shiny heads appeared in trees nearby. The juveniles scrutinized me carefully from two different trees then climbed rapidly up and up towards the upper branches of two *Symphonia globulifera* trees, no doubt to eat the tender young leaves.

This then was a perfect demonstration of how quickly the apparent ferocity of the gorillas can be replaced by affable indifference. The group were now apparently ignoring me completely and getting on with the serious business of feeding. Just as I was rejoicing at this happy turn of events I heard a silverback in the distant forest give a series of 'hoots' followed immediately by a chest-beat and ground thump. Although the animal must have been some five hundred metres away I could still hear the ground thump clearly, and later found that it had even been picked up by my tiny cassette recorder.

The reaction of the group below was instantaneous. Those in the trees began to descend while those on the ground began to move off. The female who had been high above my head paused for a moment when she was level with my position and again stared intently at me. Just then another hoot series followed by a loud, two-beat chest-beat rang out, this time from not quite so far away. The female slid rapidly down the trunk and disappeared. Yet another hoot series and chest-beat was heard and this time one of the animals below me, it sounded like Kelele, gave a sort of questioning pig-grunt. Someone was obviously still feeding but others were quite definitely moving away. As another hoot series and chest-beat rang out, now even closer, several animals gave questioning pig-grunts. One gave some strange questioning yips, tinged with overtones of fear, then seemed to be defaecating violently. There was now a scurry of movement as the remaining animals moved quickly away from the base of my tree and soon all was quiet again.

However, this did not last for long as the approaching silver-back once more gave his display. From the ground thumps he was obviously now much closer and barely two hundred metres away. I wondered whether this was the male who was often peripheral to the group, or perhaps a complete stranger who had heard their vocalizations. I decided to join Patrice and Atanazi to see if we could find somewhere from which to observe any meeting which might take place. Patrice and Atanazi were relieved to see me all in one piece and Patrice gave thanks to Mungu (God) that I was safe – his prayers had been answered. Although it was irreverent of me, the thought of the old rascal praying made me chuckle as we hurried through the swamp trying to find a vantage place.

Patrice had found the night nests in the forest at the edge of the swamp. He quickly explained what had happened. The gorillas had walked along the edge of the swamp the previous evening until they found a suitable nesting place, then this morning they had retraced their steps for some way before turning into the swamp. Thus we had mistakenly followed their trail as one continuous day journey. As we talked we searched in vain for somewhere high enough to look over the swamp, for we could hear that the group had once more left the forest and were crossing another arm of the swamp. It was hopeless, the swamp itself was flat and the trees around its edges offered no hope of a view. I decided to go and examine the nest site.

I was surprised to see that the group had nested in extremely damp conditions not far from the edge of the swamp. Although many of the nests were above ground some consisted of no more than hollow depressions in the ground around the base of a large tree. It looked as though four or five animals had slept almost pressed against each other without bothering to make nests. The nearby vegetation was not altogether ideal for nest building anyway since much of it was brittle and broke easily when touched. It would be hardly surprising if the gorillas caught pneumonia when sleeping in these conditions, and I hoped that the infants had clung tightly to their mothers for warmth.

My thoughts were suddenly interrupted by an outbreak of screams not far away. 'They are returning here!' Patrice exclaimed. Silently we retreated and tried to find a safer place to wait. There were more and more screams, some long and drawn-out as though made in anguish and ending in owl-like screeches. We crossed yet another tiny arm of the swamp and sat on a fallen tree trunk to listen to the mêlée. I switched on my cassette recorder as pandemonium broke out again. On Visoke I had heard similar short outbreaks but this was obviously something far more serious. Loud pig-grunts, barks, chest-beats, screams, ground thumps, hoot series with chest-beats followed one another in rapid succession.

Occasionally one animal would screech as though in fear or pain, and from the sounds it seemed that it was being chased up and down the hillside. So intensive was the outbreak that it did not cease even when it began to rain fifty minutes later. The screams gradually got fainter and fainter as the animals moved further and further away, but each time I thought the squabble was over it would burst out again. Eventually, almost two hours after it had begun, the trouble seemed to be over. I waited for a further thirty minutes but heard only the occasional cracking of branches as the animals resumed their feeding. These noises faded as the group moved on and the birds took up their songs, no doubt rejoicing that the row was over at last. But what had it all been about? I had most of it on my recorder but I had not been able to *see* a single thing. That it had, indeed, been violent was confirmed the next day when we examined the trail. A large area of forest on a hillside had been completely flattened. Patrice whistled in surprise. Then he and Atanazi acted in comic mime how they imagined the gorillas had chased each other. When we examined the area closely we found masses of watery dung, and in one spot the bright streaks of blood. Perhaps the outsider was trying to take away some of the females? Unfortunately I would never know, but this seemed the most likely explanation.

CHAPTER FOURTEEN

Daily wanderings

These disturbing events evidently had a profound effect on the migrations of Kelele's group and I was determined to follow them as closely as possible. They headed directly north-north-east for the next ten days, passing through areas in which they had spent long periods during April, and eventually reached the forests near the tea plantation of Mbayo some five kilometres away as the crow flies. These forests were identical to those in the area they had just vacated near Bukulumisa, and, as in the larger part of the area on the eastern border of the park, the vegetation consisted mainly of secondary growth in various stages of regeneration. For the rest of May the group restricted their movements to an area of less than two square kilometres among the lush secondary growth near the edge of the park. They fed extensively on the abundant herbs such as several species of *Lactuca* and *Helichrysum*, but by far the major part of their diet was made up of vines such as *Basella alba, Taccaza floribunda, Toxocarpus racemosus*, and above all 'Mushe'. Many other species were also eaten but in comparatively small amounts.

During the next few months my list of food plants exceeded the thirty or so recorded for the Virunga gorillas, then reached fifty, sixty, until eventually I recorded 104 different plants which were eaten in some degree by the Kahuzi gorillas. No doubt more are also sampled but the indications were clear: the Kahuzi gorillas were much more catholic in their tastes than their Virunga neighbours. They did, however, have a much wider variety from which to choose.

Even though they ate so many different items it never ceased to amaze me just how careful the gorillas were in selecting their particular food plants. In many cases several species of vines, each with remarkably similar leaves, would grow completely entwined. Yet out of such a tangled mixture the gorillas would carefully pick the leaves of perhaps *Basella alba* or *Toxocarpus racemosus* while ignoring leaves of the other species. I wanted to know *why* they did this, for some of the rejected plants looked just as succulent as those which were eaten. It was, of course, possible that some rejected plants were poisonous but it was unlikely that this was so in every case. Therefore, were some plants more nutritious than others, and if so, how did the gorillas pick an adequate and balanced diet for their huge frames? Could it also involve taste? This was a possibility since I found, as Schaller had done, that most of the plants tasted quite bitter, but others like the *Cyperus* reeds were relatively tasteless, to me at least. How could I gauge the influence of such a subjective phenomenon, and in non-human animals?

In order to try to be able to answer some of these questions I began to collect samples of plants which were readily available to the gorillas. I included both specimens of plants which were eaten by the gorillas and some of those which were not. On the advice of nutritional experts from the London School of Tropical Medicine and Hygiene I carefully dried the samples in an incubator, sealed them in polythene bags and stored them surrounded by silica gel crystals to prevent uptake of further water, until I could take them home for a detailed chemical analysis.

Meanwhile I continued to monitor the daily wanderings of the group. The start of June saw them still in the forest near Mbayo where they stayed for a further ten days meandering back and forth, sometimes over the same localized area they utilized in late May. I had some wonderful contacts and several times I was able to watch them build their night nests and then see their 'grand levée' the following morning. On 10 June the group suddenly turned south and travelled to the borders of yet another swamp where they fed extensively on the basal parts of *Cyperus* reeds. The early rainy season was now over and the June sun shone warmly for many hours each day. I suspected that the group were taking advantage of the high water content of the reeds. With such marked seasonality of rainfall would I now see different journey patterns? I began to hope so.

The group turned westwards and started to travel around the northern edge of the swamp. This stretched for several kilometres almost reaching the great Musisi, to which no doubt it was once joined. I told Adrien Deschryver that I hoped they would travel right round the back of the swamp, for there were large areas of primary mature forest in that region together with patches of swamp forest, a large grassy meadow and areas of bamboo. Laughingly he told me that it was a difficult region to traverse: it would be fine for my study but not so suitable for his tourists, so he hoped they would not do this.

To my delight and Adrien's chagrin, the group continued to travel westwards through the primary forest. They spent four days of the third week in June travelling back and forth between one area of the swamp and the nearby forests. Although they fed extensively on the *Cyperus* reeds, and even spent many hours resting among them in the midday sunshine, they never once spent the night in the swamp. Although most productive in terms of ecological data the vegetation of this area made direct observations extremely difficult. The primary forest was dark and the gorillas travelled through most of it quite quickly. When they did pause to climb some of the trees, especially those in the wet swamp forest, I had to get very close before I could see them because of the dense nature of the vegetation. Not surprisingly the gorillas then became very nervous and often I would spend hours trying to creep quietly to a good viewing position only to be spotted by one of the group. As he raised the alarm the rest of the group invariably slid rapidly to the ground and Kelele would charge.

Kelele's charges came to be very much a part of my life, for they happened virtually every day. As usual he would sound ferocious, almost as though he were going to come and tear me limb from limb, but, as usual, he always stopped. I used Adrien's technique of flattening the vegetation in a small circle whenever we made a contact. If, as in some cases, the vegetation was far too dense for a contact in the place where the gorillas were actually feeding or resting I would start to flatten the vegetation in an area nearby and then call Kelele to announce my presence. I always felt terribly self-conscious as I cried out, 'Come, come, come, come, Bwana mkubwa, come,' as though I were calling a pet dog. However, it always filled me with delight and excitement to hear Kelele's roaring reply, followed by his thundering approach.

Usually he would stop at the edge of the open circle, then either stand up and give a chest-beat or slap the nearby vegetation. One day, however, he did not stop as usual but burst out into the open circle. Then, with an amazing demonstration of agility, as though realizing he had overrun himself, he turned a backward cartwheel virtually on the spot. One can only describe his subsequent actions in anthropomorphic terms. He seemed uneasy almost to the point of embarrassment and stood there jerking his head from side to side as though avoiding my gaze. He appeared to be debating just what to do next. As I took his picture he jerked his head sharply when the shutter clicked loudly. Then, after a few more nervous head jerks he stood up bipedally, beat his chest with a rapid resonant 'pok-a-pok-a-pok-a-pok-a-pok' and, rolling sideways as he fell, he retreated under cover.

As though I no longer existed he then proceeded to feed, nonchalantly collecting several handfuls of *Basella alba* and pushing them wholesale into his cavernous mouth. The rest of the group soon joined him and eventually they completely encircled our little 'island' of flattened vegetation. None of the others ventured to leave the dense cover except to climb in the safety of nearby shrubs and trees from where they peered inquisitively down at us. Apparently satisfied they then climbed higher to feed. Although my presence obviously influenced their local movements and behaviour I felt it was only to a minor degree, for they were only moving from one patch of vegetation to another similar patch nearby and not from one vegetation type to another. They were still free to choose whether or not they actually came to see me. It was always exciting when they did, and bitterly disappointing if they did not.

The day journeys of the group, i.e. from one night nest site to the next, had so far been of the same order of magnitude as I had recorded for the Visoke gorillas. They ranged from a mere two hundred metres or so to one and a half kilometres, with a mean of just over half a kilometre per day. On 26 June this pattern changed dramatically as the group went for a long walk of over two and a half kilometres. By this date they had completely circled the large swamp, thereby extending their home range to over twenty square kilometres, almost three times bigger than the largest home range I had recorded for the gorillas on Mt Visoke. I now expected that the group would turn eastwards around the southern tip of the swamp. To my complete surprise they headed westwards to reach yet another swamp. Unlike the others this was in a later stage of succession and young saplings of *Hypericum lanceolatum* and *Rapanea pulchra* grew in abundance, consequently the ground level was slightly higher and somewhat drier. At one point on the gorillas' trail it was quite clear that one or more of them had pulled away some of the dry vegetation to expose a tiny trickle of water flowing underneath. It seemed most likely that the gorillas had been drinking to supplement their lower intake of water from the drier vegetation and to balance the heavier losses their jet-black bodies must be sustaining in the hotter dry season.

The bark of the *Rapanea* trees had not been touched by these gorillas although it had been eaten by the Virunga gorillas. I therefore added this to my list of known food plants of other gorillas which were rejected by some of the Kahuzi gorillas. This list now included such species as *Afromomum sanguinium, Alangium chinense, Rubus* sp. (blackberry), *Lobelia gibberoa,* and *Momordica foetida*. Surprisingly, *Galium simense* was only very rarely eaten by the Kahuzi gorillas. Was this because it was a different species from that eaten by the Virunga gorillas, *G. simense* rather than *G. spurium*? This seemed unlikely for the two appeared virtually identical except under the closest examination. A more likely explanation, which would explain other differences also, seemed to be that these species were far less abundant than others such as *Urera* sp., or *Basella alba* and *Taccaza floribunda*. I therefore kept a careful check on the local abundance of plants which were eaten and of known food items which were not eaten by the Kahuzi gorillas.

After travelling westwards through the densely overgrown

swamp for almost a kilometre the gorilla trail suddenly turned back on itself and headed uphill through the primary montane forest. Near the top of the hill it circled round and headed back down again. It was here that I found what I suspected the gorillas were looking for – bamboo. A few paces further on my suspicions were confirmed. Near a large mature bamboo stem we found a young shoot which had been freshly dug up. Several of the outer hairy bracts had been discarded and the tender white pith had been bitten. I carefully measured the remaining portion of the shoot. It was almost five centimetres in diameter where it had been broken off from the rest of the underground shoot, but it tapered sharply to a narrow point and was only eight centimetres long. Even allowing for the small portion which had been eaten it was quite clear that the tip of the shoot could not have been showing above the ground. How then had the gorillas detected it? We searched around for other shoots near the bases of nearby mature stems. Not finding any above the ground we used pangas to dig in likely places. Twenty minutes and almost as many holes later we dug up another shoot, a poor return for expending so much energy. How had the gorilla managed to find his shoot by digging only one hole? We searched the entire area and discovered that the gorillas were not infallible after all, for several digging spots had failed to yield a tender bamboo shoot. However, it was quite obvious that the success rate of the gorillas was far better than our own. Here then were several fascinating questions. Did the gorillas 'know' that there were bamboos in this area? Did they 'expect' them to have new shoots at this time of the year? How did they detect the new shoots?

For the remaining days of June the group travelled through the area of the overgrown swamp. They ate lots of *Cyperus*, masses of indigestible looking bark from old woody vines like *Schefflera adolphi-frederici*, and several species of *Ficus* as well as many other plants which were available in the primary forest such as *Piper capense*, *Carappa grandiflora*, and *Coffea* sp. They also ate their more common food items whenever these were available and bamboo shoots wherever these were found. They even ate more surprising things like the unsavoury looking pith of giant tree ferns such as *Cyathea manniana*. Several species of small epiphytic ferns also featured in their diet at this time, together with three species of semi-parasites.

At the beginning of July the group turned back eastwards and after seven days' travel they were again near the cultivation on the border of the park. There they added yet another new food item to their menu, the fruits of Bwamba (*Myrianthus holstii*). These compound fruits were as yet only apple-sized and still green and unripe. They were extremely bitter and made my mouth feel completely dry after only one tiny bite. The gorillas were obviously eating large quantities of them for we found many partially eaten remains on the trail. However, I wondered just what they could be getting out of the fruits for I found much of the tough green covering, together with the hard cherry-like seeds, present and seemingly undigested, intact in the gorilla dung. I recalled finding masses of unripe and undigested blackberry fruits in the dung of the Visoke gorillas and could offer no logical explanation, certainly not based on nutritional grounds for either case.

As the *Myrianthus* fruits became more abundant and riper during the later part of July they featured more and more in the gorillas' diet. On some occasions the dung near the night nests would be filled with the hard seeds. These were protected from the gorillas' digestive juices and no doubt, as I had found with the *Pygeum* fruits on Mt Visoke, were spread by the gorillas to eventually germinate in the nutritionally rich manure. Was this an example of 'mutualism' which had arisen between the gorillas and the *Myrianthus* during their co-evolution? Probably the seeds, like those of many other plants, needed to pass through an animal's alimentary canal before they could germinate.

The *Myrianthus* trees did not grow abundantly but were scattered about the eastern edge of the park, particularly in areas of very old secondary growth or secondary/primary mixtures. As I continued to map the daily travels of the group it was fascinating to see the way the pattern of their movements was changing again. Their day journeys now increased significantly in length during July and August and took them over far greater areas than any I had seen in April, May or June; in some places their trails from many days, some a week or more apart, intersected giving the appearance of 'crossroads'. At each such 'crossroad' there was a *Myrianthus* tree, or several in a tiny area. The group were obviously travelling around their range visiting each tree in turn, harvesting the available fruit before going on to the next, and now they were clearly selecting mainly the ripe fruit. By the time they returned to the first tree it was full of more ripe fruit.

When the group reached a *Myrianthus* tree they would almost all climb high up into the branches to collect the fruit. Kelele often started by eating some of the fruit which had already fallen from the tree and others which his companions had dislodged during their climbing. I thought how sensible of him it was to save his energy in such a way, but his ground search was a highly dangerous practice, for he constantly winced as many heavy fruits, now the size of grapefruits, dropped all around him! However, this practice would minimize competition between the group members for the available food. Eventually, when the fallen fruit was all eaten, he, too, would climb. Sometimes he would walk out along a narrow branch and stand bipedally to stretch for and pull down another fruit-bearing branch. I would half close my eyes and wait for the inevitable crack of the branch. Many times I expected it to mark Kelele's downfall and then hear the mighty thud as his two-hundred-kilogram frame hit the ground, but he was obviously too experienced a *Myrianthus* collector to let this happen and never once did he fall. Neither did Joe Brown, who even dared to climb among the upper branches and out towards the growing tips. Balancing carefully on swaying branches only five or six centimetres in diameter he would reach out with one long arm and bend the fruit-bearing branch tips inwards to secure his prize. Then he would carry this to a more stable position, usually in a main fork, to eat. While collecting, and especially when leaving a *Myrianthus* tree in order to keep up with the rest of the group, many of the gorillas would place one or more fruits in between their open jaws or in one hand. Thus encumbered they would clamber down to eat the hoard in a safe place or while travelling along the trail after their more impatient companions. We often found the discarded, half-eaten remains of *Myrianthus* fruits considerable distances away from the trees.

The group's wanderings took them through many different vegetation types, one of which to my astonishment turned out to be a tiny plantation of marijuana, which was obviously being carefully cultivated, no doubt by Patrice's friends and perhaps even by Patrice himself! He laughingly denied all ownership and pointed out the remarkable fact that he only very rarely smoked, i.e. when he was *given* some! Pretending this small violation of the sanctity of the park did not exist we continued to follow the gorillas' trail. I was relieved to find that they, too, had not dallied to sample the delights and dangers of the drug, for their trail passed alongside the neat rows of plants and continued in a straight line back into the forest.

Several times the group made further exploratory sallies westwards into the patches of bamboo forest which grew on the higher ground. Again they dug for shoots and even their already high success rate began to improve as fewer and fewer holes failed to yield a succulent new shoot. When the growing shoots began to appear above the ground in late August and early September after the start of the late rains, the whole orientation of the journeys changed yet again. From being predominantly north–south along the eastern border of the park between Mbayo and Tshibinda it now turned east–west. As September advanced it became more and more compressed in a north–south direction and extended further and further westwards into newer, more extensive areas of bamboo forest. The group, however, made several trips back eastwards, for the Bwamba harvest was not yet over and they came to eat their fill before returning to the new crop of bamboo shoots in the west.

It was during the Bwamba fruiting season that Kelele again charged out of dense cover into the open. Once more he seemed uncertain what to do next and again avoided staring directly at me. Finally he charged off sideways, half rising to beat his chest. Then, apparently unperturbed, he returned to the

Bwamba feast. His reputation had now spread rapidly over Africa and, indeed, the whole world, no doubt helped by the tales of the Hollywood film crew and other film makers who had visited us. Thus more and more tourists came to Kahuzi. All wanted specifically to experience the thrills of being subjected to one of Kelele's spectacular charges while knowing (or hoping) that it was safe. Adrien was always there with his rifle; but that knowledge did not prevent one tourist, no doubt suitably impressed by Kelele's display, from wetting his trousers! He joined the list of many satisfied visitors to Kahuzi-Biega who would remember more than just the gorillas, for there were swamps, hills, safari ants and worst of all stinging hornets to add extra spice to their jungle safari. They could also see bushbuck, monkeys, hornbills, sunbirds and dozens of other shy creatures of the forest if they were lucky and with careful trackers. Only one group was fortunate enough to catch glimpses of the chimpanzees which roamed the regions of primary forest, but several others heard their raucous cries which were probably given when a tree full of ripe fruit was located.

I found several more examples of chimpanzees digging for underground bees' nests and was even fortunate enough to collect some fresh chimpanzee dung. It contained the remains of wax comb and of literally hundreds of bees. No doubt the more tender non-chitinous larvae, which must have been eaten with some of the comb, had been completely digested. In two different samples I also found the undigested, chitinous, exoskeletons of thousands of ants belonging to the genus *Crematogaster*. These are tree-living ants and usually build their nests high above the ground. It seemed more likely that the chimps were after the tender larvae rather than the adults with their 'armour-plated' bodies. Many other food items of plant origin were present and I added these to my list of the food eaten by species other than gorillas, especially other primates. It soon became obvious that the various primates present avoided much direct competition with each other, often by eating different foods. Where the same plant was eaten, different animals ate different parts, some the bark, some the leaves, some the shoots. To some extent vertical zonation of feeding layers throughout the forest strata also helped to reduce competition between the many primate species, since only the smallest monkeys are able to scale the taller trees and reach the tender shoots of slender branch tips. However, the more generalized anatomy of the chimps and gorillas enabled them also to explore several layers of the three-dimensional forest strata. In addition the immense strength of the gorillas enabled them to tear apart larger and tougher food items like wild banana trees, branches of *Hagenia abyssinica* or bamboo shoots.

During September the new bamboo shoots grew rapidly but were still quite soft. Lignification of the tissues had not yet taken place and even shoots several metres high could easily be snapped off, especially at their main growing point just under the surface of the soil. The gorillas' trail through the bamboo forests was littered by hundreds of such broken shoots. Most of them had chunks of the basal nodal pith chewed away or, as they grew taller, some of their bracts were discarded and the pith from several nodes removed. Still older stems were usually broken and split open. Occasionally the gorillas would scrape the pith from the entire inner curved surfaces of the split shoot with their incisor teeth, but usually only the pith of the nodes, or even the entire node, was eaten. The scattered remains of peeled bracts and broken stems soon littered the whole of the bamboo zone. Much of it began to decay rapidly, while other intact shoots nearby, together with new ones just appearing above the ground, carried on the annual replacement of the bamboo forest. The gorillas often appeared to be extremely wasteful in their feeding on the bamboo shoots, for I frequently found many broken shoots with only one tiny bite taken from them or nothing eaten at all. I could see no reason for such rejections and could only conclude that faced with such a superabundance of choice the gorillas were being ultra selective, choosing only those shoots which tasted, or looked to be, in the best condition.

By the middle of September the Bwamba harvest was over at last, but by now the new bamboo shoots were rapidly popping up all over the bamboo zones, and once more the gorilla group altered their pattern of movements. Forsaking even the occasional visit back to the Bwamba trees they focused their entire wanderings on the area of the old swamp and its many patches of bamboo forest on the higher ground nearby. When September gave way to October my maps of their trails began to look more and more like tightly tangled yarns of wool as the gorillas frequently crossed and re-crossed their own trails in an area of swamp and forest covering only some two square kilometres. Their daily inter-nest distances, which had reached a peak in September with a mean of almost one and a half kilometres per day (one journey alone being over three kilometres), now rapidly decreased to a mean of one kilometre per day. As October progressed this was lowered even further and sometimes I found consecutive night nest sites literally within a hundred metres of each other. Several were adjacent to previous nest sites. On such occasions it was impossible to measure or even estimate reasonably the actual distance covered each day by the group for their trails became so criss-crossed that they were impossible to disentangle.

Although many of the gorillas built their individual nests out of mature bamboo stems the group never once nested for the night in a patch of single-stand bamboo forest; they always travelled to the bamboo-forest interface to find a suitable nest site. Since a lack of suitable nesting material was not the likely cause of such behaviour I concluded that they did not like to spend prolonged periods at night in the more open and exposed regions of bamboo. John Emlen had noticed similar behaviour by a group of gorillas for seven consecutive days in the Mt Muhavura region: while they fed on the higher bamboo-covered slopes during the day they always descended at night to nest in the primary montane forest on the lower slopes.

The group fed extensively in the swamp as well as in the nearby bamboo forest. I found that the members were spread much further apart at this time of the year and in these vegetation types than they were when they were in open secondary vegetation during the early wet season. Sometimes they were split into sub-groups up to two hundred metres apart, some feeding in the swamp itself while the others were in the bamboo forest. Even when the entire group was among the bamboos they were scattered as each animal foraged alone. I found it much more difficult to observe the group at this time of the year than at any other time, even though by now the group were well habituated to me after almost daily contacts during the past six months.

During previous years Adrien Deschryver had stopped contacting the gorillas when they went into the bamboo zone; he said that it was too dangerous, for then the gorillas became really 'wild' again. I, of course, could not abandon their trail at such an important time so he allowed me to continue, duly forewarned. I did find that when the gorillas were in the bamboo forest they seemed to become much more nervous, the males in particular. On contact Kelele would run screaming at me through the tangled bamboo stems smashing them like straws as he charged, The old, dead stems were brittle and cracked like machine-gun fire as he ran relentlessly through them. One day he charged at me in this manner three times in succession. The third time he got so close that to stop himself from finally colliding with me he stood up when only a metre away and clutched at a nearby bamboo stem for support. I was now so used to his charges that I continued to take pictures of him. He swung his right arm in an arc towards me, his huge curved fist swishing past only thirty centimetres from my stomach. I involuntarily breathed in, feeling like a toreador executing a *paso doble*. As he reached forward the bamboo stem, an old moss-covered dead specimen, broke under his immense weight and he dropped down again on all fours. He stood there panting gently like a dog while I wound on and tried to focus my camera to take his picture. He was so close that the zoom lens, even at its smallest focal length of eighty millimetres, would not focus properly. Nevertheless I took a picture which, although it was slightly out of focus, constantly reminds me of those charges and how at the end of them he stood quadrupedally nearby, again apparently ill at ease and 'wondering' what to do next.

I had no doubt provoked the charges because I had been rather relentlessly creeping forward in order to be able to see the group more clearly while they were resting at the edge of the bamboo forest. In the meantime Patrice and Atanazi were waiting some ten metres behind me. They had seen the charges clearly and Patrice was impressed that I had stood my ground so confidently. I myself had been even more impressed by the sheer size of Kelele's head, which at such close range as I had just experienced was truly enormous. Trying to gauge its size against Patrice's own tiny frame I spaced my hands apart from the top of his own head down to his stomach. I laughed and said, 'Kelele's head is enormous! He would be able to eat little Patrice easily, like this!' Never outdone in such flippant exchanges, Patrice coolly replied, 'Yes, Bwana, I know, I have already eaten three like him!'

I countered by pointing out that now I had taken pictures of Kelele charging at me I wanted something even more spectacular, say of him holding and eating Patrice! I added that I would pay Patrice a huge reward if he would enable me to take such pictures. Atanazi was doubled up with laughter at such a suggestion, but Patrice, with a twinkle in his deep brown eyes, had a better one of his own. 'No, Bwana, I think that you can make another excellent picture. You take a picture of *me* when I am eating that old gorilla, and I will pay *you* a good reward!' At this Atanazi collapsed with sobs of laughter. I, too, now twice defeated by Patrice's skilful humour, surrendered to my mirth. As we laughed loudly together we heard Kelele add his defiant roar while he shepherded his flock safely away from these other strange primates and their even stranger vocalizations.

As October progressed, fewer and fewer new shoots of bamboo appeared, while the older ones, now up to four and five metres high, became more and more lignified and hence stronger and tougher. As they did so the gorillas became more selective. Wrenching them over with one easy jerk they would then bend the stems until they split open. Then tearing them apart with wonderfully co-ordinated actions of their hands, jaws and teeth they would excise only tiny amounts of tender pith from the nodes, rather in the manner of a gourmet eating an artichoke.

At this time they began to turn some of their attention from the maturing bamboo to the cherry-like fruits of the huge

Syzygium guinense trees which grew in the swamp forest on the hills bordering the old swamp. They also made occasional forays into patches of secondary forest which was now bursting out in rapid re-growth after the start of the late rains. The change of diet of the gorillas was reflected in their dung. From being a runny, watery mass of almost exclusively tiny fibres of bamboo shoots it now began to regain its firmer, lobe-shaped structure as undigested leaf remnants and long dark fibres bound it together. The seeds of *Syzygium* fruits were sometimes present in the dung in large numbers, just as the Bwamba seeds had been earlier in the year.

My time, and mainly my funds, were rapidly running out. It now looked as though the gorillas would move back into the areas of secondary forest which they had abandoned when the dry season started. I visited some of these areas and found them to be almost unrecognizable since I had last seen them in June. Our trails were overgrown, and known nest sites, which had been stark, dry scars for many weeks, were now almost hidden by the lush fresh growth of rampant herbs and vines. Favoured gorilla foods, especially 'Mushe', abounded. Patrice, forever the oracle, agreed. 'They will return here soon, perhaps next month, like last year and every year.' Thus it appeared that the cycle of the gorillas' journeys was almost over, and was now starting again with the patterns I had seen during the early rainy season in April. The late rains would now last until June, with perhaps a brief dry spell in December or January. The secondary growth, however, would remain lush until the main dry season the following July and August, when the Bwamba fruits would appear once more, to be followed by the bamboo shoots with the September rains.

I had been so impressed by Kelele's charges, now more and more into the open, that I persuaded Adrien Deschryver that what we wanted was a picture of Kelele charging and screaming at someone, preferably at Adrien! Unlike Patrice, Adrien was forever willing to try almost any suggestion, even the seemingly impossible, and especially the downright dangerous. One day therefore we followed the group specifically with the objective of obtaining such pictures. We eventually found them resting among a dense stand of bamboo. Adrien set up his tape recorder to record whatever happened. I wondered whether it was in case neither of us survived! Unfortunately, by now Kelele was so used to being contacted, even in the bamboo, that we had to persuade him to charge by noisily pulling down some of the vegetation hanging on to the bamboo stems across the trail. I was standing back with camera at the ready while Adrien frantically pulled down more and more vegetation to make a noise. Unimpressed, Kelele carried on feeding from a bamboo shoot. Adrien pulled down more vegetation and this time a brittle bamboo stem broke with a loud crack. Kelele's reaction was instantaneous; dropping the bamboo he was clutching he charged straight at Adrien. Less than two metres away he stopped, stood partially bipedally and screamed. This was the moment I had nervously been waiting for. I pressed the shutter release.

Kelele dropped down again on all fours and paused for a moment. Adrien nervously murmured to me, 'Take another, take another.' Later the tape recording had to be edited to erase my reply, for I had already tried to wind on only to find I had reached the end of that roll of film! Thus the situation became farcical as I frantically tried to rewind and insert a new film before Kelele did anything else. I had not even got the old film out before he stood up again, and screaming loudly, slapped at the vegetation near Adrien's head. Then he turned away, stalked ponderously through a patch of the rampant herbs and sat down six metres away. In addition to my 'expletive deleted' we later found that the tape recorder had recorded an anxious comment from Adrien, 'My heart has stopped! My heart has stopped!' Such was the impressive nature of Kelele's so-called 'bluff' charge!

At the end of October when it was, indeed, clear that the group were now alternating between the bamboo forest and the areas of secondary forest, and spending more and more time in the latter, I regretfully called my study of them to a halt. Even the final contact was a memorable one, and several tourists were present. They were not disappointed for Kelele dutifully gave his spectacular charge. He was now often referred to rather flippantly as 'Casimir' by Adrien, because like Michael Casimir he had reddish hair, although Kelele's grew only in one narrow band across his beetling brows – in a manner similar to the reddish patch of Geronimo, the silverback leader of Group 9 on Mt Visoke. The third youngest male, who had previously been quite shy on contact, usually only giving away his presence by his shrill screaming threat barks, also showed himself to peer inquisitively at Adrien. Kelele came to stare at Adrien from behind a dense shrub, and as I watched this exchange of glances I looked around for Patrice. He was busy drawing the attention of some of the tourists to the antics of a young infant who had climbed up a nearby shrub in order to observe our own human group. I felt an overwhelming sense of gratitude and love for all three, Patrice, Adrien and Kelele, for the trust they had given me and the wonderful memories we had shared together in this their forest world.

Peter and Irene Kunkel were also in my thoughts at this time, for to them also I owed so much. I was glad that I had been able to take them out to see my study group and Kelele had given them also a day to remember. But I knew that they were now extremely sad. After many years of hard and often frustrating work spent building up the institute after its decline during the troubled sixties, they, too, would soon be leaving Africa. To them Zaire was more than just a place in which to do research, it was very much their home. Peter had been replaced as Director General of IRSAC by a Zairois Director, Dr Ntika Nkumu, and had therefore decided to take the Volkswagen programme of research on tropical forest ecology to another venue, perhaps Central America. The institute, however, and especially Tshibati, would never seem the same without Peter. There I had enjoyed so many meals, and had so many stimulating conversations with visitors who came from all over the globe, that I nicknamed their dining room the 'international room'.

Now, as I sat in the forest, frustrating communication barriers prevented the expression of my true feelings to animals and humans alike. Even to Adrien and Peter, who spoke excellent English, I found I could not convey my thanks as I would have wished. I knew that I would desperately miss them all when I returned to the now unreal world of England.

Margaret and I were exhausted after the intense nature of the study during the past year. We were therefore delighted to have a brief relaxing holiday in Zaire's beautiful 'Parc National des Virungas' (formerly Parc Albert). On our return to IRSAC we discovered that two of the Volkswagen's kombies had to be driven to Mombasa. Hans and Hilda Schlichte were to drive one, and we readily agreed to accompany them and drive the other. The journey of over three thousand kilometres from the centre of Africa eastwards to the coast was an experience we will never forget, for it added a perfect ending to a truly memorable period in our lives. We saw other parks, met other scientists and game wardens and discussed their difficulties and aspirations, to find that they were very similar to our own. All around us we saw the vastness of Africa, its immense variety of habitats and their wildlife; its problems and potentials.

We visited Olduvai Gorge and were greatly impressed by the courage and dedication it must have taken to spend a lifetime working in such hot, dry and dusty conditions as the Leakeys had done. I tried to picture it all as he must have seen it in his imaginative mind's eye, full of large herds of game species now long extinct and, above all, the home of primitive man. It was fascinating to see the exposed digs with their *in situ* collections of bones and artifacts and to try and imagine what it had been like there over a million years earlier. Was this really the birthplace of man? If so, what was the subsequent course of his evolution? Or had he evolved further north in Ethiopia and then moved south? There were still so many secrets that Africa had yet to yield to enquiring minds. They were still locked up in fossil strata, buried beneath ancient lakes or hidden in remote forests, but they were there waiting to be found. I pondered upon all I had seen as I relaxed at our journey's end in the warm waters of the Indian Ocean at Mombasa. I knew that when I returned to England, Africa would always be calling me back.

Unfortunately, all too soon we had to forsake this tropical paradise and return to the chill of an English December. Once the New Year started it was time to get down to the serious and somewhat daunting task of sorting out my data and writing up my thesis. It is the fear of many research workers, students and old hands alike that their precious data will either get lost or be stolen! When one considers the time and effort spent collecting it, often as a result of unique opportunities, this is an understandable phobia. I had carefully stored all my data in labelled folders which just fitted neatly into a large cardboard box which I used for a filing cabinet, keeping it under my desk in the bedroom of our pavilion at IRSAC. On our first night at home I woke up in a cold sweat screaming, 'No, no . . . Oh no!' for I dreamt that in my hasty packing I had forgotten to bring my box of data with me. In my mind's eye I could still see it standing under my desk back at IRSAC. My cries roused a very startled Margaret, and I immediately realized that my unconscious fears had expressed themselves in a nightmare – but I got out of bed and checked just to be certain!

I spent the next two years analysing my data and writing up my thesis. Eventually the draft copy was completed and comments were made upon it by various advisers. At long last I took four copies to the binders and handed them over feeling rather like Eamon Andrews saying, 'This is your life!'

At my viva the very experienced examiners, Drs John Crook and Ron Pearson, knew how to put me at my ease yet stretch my data, my understanding and my nerves to their limits – and beyond! Several agonizing hours later when they offered their congratulations and told me I had passed I was filled with an overwhelming sense of relief. It was as if a whole era had suddenly ended, an era in which I had shared the wanderings of the gorillas and become part of their family. I had learned far more than just aspects of the behaviour and ecology of gorillas. I had learned more about people, including myself; and I had learned that the secrets of nature are far more beautiful and complex than any writer can ever express.

CHAPTER FIFTEEN

Whose forests are these?

Many studies of animal behaviour had concentrated on showing how similar each individual of a particular species is in the way it behaves. But I was also interested in differences in behaviour, differences between populations, between groups as well as between individual animals, for here one could find clues as to just how well adapted the gorillas were to their forest habitat. Unfortunately, Schaller's findings on the behaviour and ecology of the Virunga gorillas were being mistakenly taken by many people as being typical of 'the' mountain gorilla. My research had now shown various differences between the Virunga and Kahuzi populations, but just *how* different were they and what were the causes of these differences? More urgently, could such differences have any implications for the future survival of the respective gorilla populations?

The most obvious differences related to the home range area of particular groups. In Kahuzi these were in the order of thirty to forty square kilometres per family group and were at least four or five times larger than those I had calculated for the groups on Mt Visoke. Overall size differences, however, may be of less importance than how each group actually *utilizes* the home range area it occupies. The home range areas of any animal, or group of animals, should provide all the requirements for a normal life: a place to shelter and sleep, opportunities to find a mate, to produce and rear offspring to maturity, and, of course, a supply of essential food. The more efficiently an animal can exploit particular food resources the more successful, in biological terms, it is likely to be. The process of evolution by natural selection has obviously produced an amazing variety of animals able to utilize a multitude of available sources of food. Their efficiency in using these sources may depend not only on anatomical and physiological adaptations but also on behavioural adaptations, i.e. the way in which they exploit them, for specific foods are unlikely to be always available in super-abundance. Thus many methods, or 'strategies' as some researchers call them, have evolved among animals enabling them to exploit the availability and distribution of the particular resources.

The points of obvious scientific interest are those relating to the influences of the environment. Which factors are involved? Which are important and which less so? How important are 'local' conditions and how adaptable are various animal species to changing conditions? I therefore compared various aspects of the daily lives of the gorillas from the two regions in relation to their utilization of their respective home ranges.

Although the daily wanderings of the Visoke gorillas appeared to be rather random affairs, my data on Group 4 showed that they spent more time in two particular areas of their home range. It was therefore possible that these were 'core areas', for each had open herb-covered slopes on which thistles, dock, nettles and bedstraw grew in abundance. The region in between the two areas contained more trees and several steep ravines and appeared to be mainly used as a transit area by Group 4 during their journeys to and from their two core areas. However, I felt that I had insufficient data to postulate any definite patterns of usage. The gorillas' day journeys did appear to be rather randomly orientated in that they sometimes spent up to seven days in similar vegetation before visiting another zone, while on other occasions they abruptly changed zones after only one day.

In contrast, the Kahuzi gorillas, especially Kelele's group, not only made significantly longer day journeys than the Visoke gorillas, but there were also quite definite patterns to be seen among their daily wanderings. Two aspects of their ranging behaviour were most obvious: (a) some areas were visited more than others; (b) some areas were visited at different times of the year. Although many factors played minor roles in influencing the course of these movements it was obvious that there was one factor of primary importance, the distribution and availability of various food items in different areas and at different times of the year.

I had also noted that the Kahuzi gorillas ate a far wider range of food items than their Virunga counterparts, and, since their forest world had many more layers or 'strata', they climbed frequently whilst exploiting the varied food resources. I finally concluded that the actual selection of food items varied between groups and even between individuals, and was influenced not only by the nutritive value of a particular food item, e.g. energy value, protein or vitamin content, but by many factors. The final selections were often a compromise and, since they varied between individual gorillas, this helped to minimize the competition for food between members of the same group; even feeding at different heights in the vegetation, by virtue of size and climbing ability of individuals, contributed to ensuring that many different resources were exploited. The various barks that were eaten were chosen, I believe, not for their nutritive value, which was often very low, but for their physical action in the gut, thus it is a source of roughage.

Therefore the feeding and ranging behaviour of the Kahuzi gorillas, their 'feeding strategy', was beautifully adapted to their local environmental conditions, and, indeed, had obviously been shaped by them. There were apparently random wanderings through large areas of secondary forest in which food was abundant and widespread; directed movements from one vegetation type to another (even one tree to another); and localized circling through areas of temporary concentrations of food abundance. The gorillas were obviously not merely 'following the food', since some of their movements had been anticipatory, especially when they were searching for the young bamboo shoots. Their wanderings, therefore, were clearly well-co-ordinated, seasonal *migrations* about their home range. In turn this may well have influenced their social structure, for a fairly stable social group of gorillas is ideal for passing on knowledge of the availability of food items from older animals to young ones by example.

In the social group other habits may also be passed on and thereby become 'cultural traditions', such as the building of nests among the available trees rather than on the ground, and even of defaecating *inside* the nests and sleeping on the dung. After considering several possibilities I finally decided that this seemingly unhygienic behaviour was a cultural tradition in the Virunga area and was used by the gorillas to insulate their nests against the freezing ground temperatures at night. Since the gorillas' dung is rather like horse manure it does not stick to their hair and provide a focus for infection, and the 'originator(s)' of such a tradition were more likely to survive the cold nights on the mountain. In Kahuzi, where the night temperatures were much higher, the habit had never evolved.

Although it may seem strange that random foraging may be part of a 'strategy' of ranging behaviour, it is obviously an alternative to systematic cropping in order to avoid the over-exploitation of some areas and the neglect of others. Thus in parts of the Virunga volcanoes region, especially where food is abundant, it may well be the main feeding strategy of much of the gorilla population. However, where the available resources vary seasonally or from place to place, or both as in Kahuzi, then other feeding strategies which are better suited to the exploitation of these variable resources will evolve. It seemed clear that if the distribution and availability of food resources were the main factors influencing the gorillas' wanderings, then the causes which made these wanderings become annual migrations were the climatic and geological factors which dictated the vegetation types found in particular regions.

I also found another major influence, that of man. Detailed vegetation maps of almost the entire area encompassed by the Kahuzi-Biega National Park had been prepared by Christine Marius, a member of the team of Belgian botanists who had recently surveyed both Kahuzi and the Virungas. These maps not only illustrated the vegetational differences in the Kahuzi-Biega area associated with altitude, climate and geology, they also clearly showed the differences in past usage of the forest to the east and west of the Mitumba mountains. In the past these had been used by two culturally different Bantu tribes, the Batembo in the west and the Bashi in the south-east.

The entire Kivu province is literally a melting pot for many ancient cultures in both Zaire and nearby Rwanda. Trying to discover both the history and the present status of these ethnic groups were several anthropologists associated with IRSAC. Among them were two young Americans who became very good friends of ours, Kathy and Dave Newbury. According to Dave the two groups nearest to the park, the Bashi and the Batembo, are only relatively recent immigrants into the area. They probably arrived from the south-west and the north-west respectively about four hundred years ago.

West of the mountains the Batembo relied heavily on the forest for their food, in the form of edible plants and game. Hunting, using dogs, nets and spears, fishing in the many rivers, and gathering plants formed the economic basis for their way of life. Some bananas and manioc were also cultivated as staples and, in some areas, small amounts of peanuts, maize and rice. The soil, however, was poor and quickly leached of nutrients by the crops and by exposure to the elements. When its productivity became too low whole village groups would move on to another area. But cutting down virgin forest was a hard task and the relatively small populations sometimes moved back to previously abandoned areas, slashed down the secondary growth and burned it in order to re-enrich the soil. After repeated burnings the soil became too degraded to support even normal secondary growth, thus species more tolerant of poor soils, especially *Pteridium* ferns, became the dominant plants in a 'deflected succession'.

East of the Mitumba mountains the soil was richer and much of the gently sloping hillsides was quickly cleared of forest by the colonizing Bashi groups. They were mainly agriculturalists rather than hunters and soon the region produced large amounts of beans, peas, maize, bananas, manioc, sweet potatoes and sorghum as their main crops. The population of this veritable garden of Eden grew rapidly and expanded westwards higher up the slopes of the mountains. The Bashi also used the traditional 'slash and burn' type of shifting agriculture but on a much larger scale than the Batembo in the west. As the population grew they cleared more and more areas of virgin montane rain forest to plant their food crops and, much later, plantations of coffee and tea. In addition to the Bashi agriculturalists, many pastoralists, mainly Rwandese immigrants fleeing from the many upheavals in nineteenth- and twentieth-century Rwanda, grazed their cows on the patches of open grassland near Lake Kivu and near the very summit of the mountain chain.

In more recent times increasing centralization of the social, administrative, and later political structure has gradually developed around Bukavu (formerly Costermansville) on the southern tip of Lake Kivu. This has caused migrations of large numbers of the Bashi population into the area. Some of the cleared forest regions, especially the less productive ones nearer the mountains, were probably abandoned and therefore gradually became covered by secondary forest growth. Even more recently, when the Kahuzi-Biega area was given official nature reserve status in 1960, agriculturalists and pastoralists were moved still further east as the boundaries of the park were officially established.

On the maps which Christine Marius had prepared the various vegetation types appeared like pieces of a complicated mosaic. The patterns of the natural altitudinal zonation were clearly visible, with montane rain forest giving way to bamboo, and eventually heath and alpine communities at higher altitudes. The long chain of swamps, each with its associated areas of swamp forest where the *Cyperus* was being replaced by forest during natural successional changes, was located in the zone of highest rainfall on the eastern slopes of the Mitumba mountains. However, the distribution of the patches of secondary growth was the most noticeable feature of the maps. In the areas inhabited by the mainly hunter-gatherer Batembo ethnic groups in the west of the mountains only a few tiny patches of secondary forest could be seen. On the other hand, the area east of the mountains, inhabited by the agricultural Bashi and pastoral Rwandese, was covered by many extensive patches of secondary regenerating forest of various ages. These ranged from new herbaceous growth in recently cleared areas to old secondary forest, almost indistinguishable from the original mature virgin forest which remained only in extremely small and rare patches.

The implications for the gorillas were enormous. I had calculated that over seventy per cent of the home range of Kelele's group at Tshibinda consisted of secondary vegetation types. In these areas the gorillas were able to find abundant succulent herbs and vines for much of the year. The forest east of the mountains, with its extensive areas of secondary vegetation, could therefore support a larger gorilla population than the larger regions of primary forest in the west. My experiences in the primary forest around Nyakalonge and then in the secondary forests on the eastern border of the park had already indicated that such differences in population numbers and distribution did in fact exist.

However, the suitability of the succulent herbs and vines in areas of open secondary forest rapidly declined during the dry season in July and August. The wanderings of Kelele's group had clearly shown that areas of mature primary forest, which were less susceptible to changes in rainfall, were important refuges for the gorillas at this time, particularly when the *Myrianthus* (Bwamba) trees came into fruit. With the coming of the late rains, the new bamboo shoots sprouted. This had the double benefit of providing sources of energy and high protein and of keeping the gorillas away from the areas of secondary forest while they regenerated rapidly with the rain. Thus gorilla groups living in the Kahuzi region had to utilize a fair balance of the many vegetation types within their home ranges if they were to survive the seasonal fluctuations in food availability, just as Kelele's group had done. The generalized anatomical structure of the gorillas and the plasticity of their behaviour and ecology has therefore not only enabled them to survive in such areas of variable forest but also to take advantage of the more abundant food in areas of secondary regenerating forest. It therefore seems likely that in such areas the gorilla population, far from declining, is actually expanding. I believe therefore that the Kahuzi forests are more typical of the habitat in which gorillas have evolved than those of the Virunga volcanoes; the gorillas there I suggest are 'atypical' in an unusual type of forest habitat, but one to which they were pre-adapted.

It is unlikely that areas of secondary regenerating forest were so abundant and extensive during the evolutionary history of the gorillas. They were probably restricted to localized pockets where mature trees had died and fallen, with perhaps more extensive areas being colonized after natural forest fires. There is also a great deal of evidence to indicate how elephants may also change the structure of some forests, for although even these huge beasts could not push giant forest trees over they could cause their premature death by tearing off their bark, thereby causing what Adriaan Kortlandt calls 'parklandization'. However, it seems clear that even the combined action of all these agencies in creating secondary forest conditions has recently been surpassed by the activities of man.

Paradoxically, it is man who on the one hand creates these areas which the gorillas find so ideal a habitat, and on the other hand threatens them with extinction. These threats take the forms familiar to all threatened species: pressures from predation, competition for space and resources, and exploitation. The result is always the same, a restriction of the species distribution and a decrease in its numbers until the populations are no longer viable units. Extinction follows rapidly – unless adequate preventative measures are taken in time.

In 1959 John Emlen and George Schaller estimated the gorilla population of the whole Virunga region to be about four hundred and fifty, in an area of some one hundred and fifty-five square miles. More recent and much more detailed surveys have been made throughout this region under the instigation of Dian Fossey. After the final survey in 1973, Alan Foulds put the total estimate at only two hundred and seventy. Since the survey covered approximately eighty-five per cent of the area, a realistic figure for the gorilla population of the whole area can only be of some three hundred animals. However, it is the actual *distribution* of these animals throughout the Virunga region which highlights some of the pressures on this population. Of the total 270 animals actually found, 183 were seen in the Zaire section, 74 in the Rwandese section and only 13 in the Ugandan section. Even allowing for the differences in area of these three sections (approximately 250 km^2, 200 km^2 and 30 km² respectively) it can be seen that the Zaire section still has a higher overall density of gorillas than its neighbouring sections.

There can be no doubt that while some of the present reasons for these differences in population density may be due to differences in the suitability of the habitat in each section, the major cause is human interference and disturbance. Despite the fact that the Virunga area contains vast stretches of unique *Hagenia* woodland, some eight thousand hectares were recently taken by the Rwandese government, cleared and used for agricultural purposes, mainly for growing pyrethrum. Anyone seeing these areas for the first time today would be amazed to think that they were recently covered in dense forest. They could be forgiven for failing to realize that this area has the rare distinction which recognizes its natural beauty and the need to protect it, the status of National Park!

If such large areas of forest continue to be cut down, the gorillas, and other animals such as elephant, buffalo, duiker, bushbuck and the few remaining leopards, will be forced higher and higher up the slopes of the volcanoes. If all the saddle areas between the peaks are eventually cultivated then the animal populations will stand, like so many islands, in an ever growing sea of cultivation. As the altitude increases so the vegetation of the area changes, not only in species composition but also in abundance; consequently the areas of suitable forage get smaller and smaller at higher altitudes. In addition some plant species have very long growth periods. A giant senecio, for example, may take up to two hundred years to reach its full size. A gorilla group which has been forced to spend more than its usual amount of time at these altitudes can destroy the tree in less than an hour while feeding on the tender pith. At these altitudes rain and mist are much more frequent than lower down the mountain and the gorillas, who merely sit still during heavy rain, have less time to find their food. In addition, pneumonia, a major cause of death of the gorillas in this region, is bound to claim more victims at the higher, wetter altitudes. Infant mortality especially will inevitably increase.

Besides this threat of isolation in poor feeding areas the

Virunga gorillas face other hazards. The boundary to the Rwanda park, now merely an overgrown ditch, means only that the cultivation ceases at that point. The park itself is constantly invaded by nearby villagers to collect wood for their huts, furniture or fires; honey gatherers frequently set fire to mature trees in order to smoke out the bees; poachers come and go daily, mainly after duiker, bushbuck and elephant, but they have recently revived the custom of killing gorillas to obtain parts of their anatomy which they believe to have magical powers. Finally, most destructive of all, the cattle keepers invade the park with their hundreds of cattle which eat and trample vast tracts of forest and transform it into a muddy waste-land.

One could put forward a seemingly realistic argument in favour of the appropriation of this parkland by the Rwandese government. The pyrethrum flowers grown in the rich volcanic soil of this area have the highest pyrethrin content of any in the world. The swing away from man-made insecticides such as DDT and other chlorinated hydrocarbons, because of their harmful side effects, created a great demand for natural insecticides such as pyrethrum, which is lethal only to insects and does not accumulate in the soil. Such a commodity is therefore a valuable source of the foreign exchange which is so vital to the economy of any developing nation, especially one so small as Rwanda. However, the situation is not as straightforward as it may seem at first sight. It is not just a simple choice of forest for the gorillas, or plantations for economic growth. The complete destruction of such vast areas of forest has already had drastic effects on the hydrology of the area. The heavy rains, which were once soaked up by the forest and gradually allowed to seep through this natural giant sponge, now race down the steep slopes removing the fertile top soil and causing severe gully erosion. Flash flooding and the silting up of rivers miles downstream quickly follows. In addition to these natural disasters no one apparently thought to investigate whether the cultivation of pyrethrum, which demands a great deal of daily care and attention, was suited to the *laissez-faire* attitude of some Rwandese farmers. Consequently production is far below the targets which were originally and ideally projected.

Therefore the short-term economic gains from the cultivation of pyrethrum may be hopelessly outweighed by the enormous long-term ecological losses. Also the short-term gains may themselves soon disappear, for an artificial pyrethrum has now been manufactured in research laboratories. Full-scale production of new synthetic insecticides with similar properties to the natural ones may soon be under way and therefore render the cultivation of pyrethrum flowers uneconomic. Unfortunately the forest cannot be so easily re-established, for nature's time scale is much slower than man's.

Thus from a wider viewpoint we are not only dealing with the imminent extinction of mountain gorillas but with the possible destruction of vast areas of their forest habitat, whose part in the water and energy cycles of both the local area and the planet as a whole we do not fully understand. We are not even dealing here with 'conservation' for this rather narrow concept is a misnomer. What we are dealing with is the good or bad *management* of the world's resources, both biotic and abiotic. It is therefore encouraging to hear the following statement from a man who not only recognizes the responsibilities of his country but is prepared to face up to them – General Mobutu Sese Seko, President of the Republic of Zaire:

> We have certain advantages in being under-equipped. We have to be proud that we have never made errors such as those which are regretted by some countries considered as completely developed. We are never disappointed not to show our guests our cathedrals or monuments because the heritage of our ancestors is the natural beauty of our country, our rivers, large streams, forests, insects, animals, lakes, volcanoes, mountains and plains. In a word, nature is the integral and real part of our originality and personality.
>
> It should not surprise you when we declare that our ambition is to make our country, Zaire, the paradise of nature. We have no intention to speculate upon public curiosity by selling the skins of crocodiles for handbags. We want first to study how these animals grow because we do not wish these animals to disappear

in our National Parks.

We desire only that when scientists will have transformed the world into an artificial one that in Zaire an authentic nature will remain . . .

Over the next few years our National Parks will be extended to over 12 to 15% of the country.

Having made the decision to increase the area available for National Parks, as Zaire has so wisely done, it is necessary to look carefully and rationally at the natural resources of all potential park areas. In this respect Zaire is an extremely fortunate country, for it has vast areas of great natural beauty and its existing eight National Parks contain a wide variety of scenery, habitats and their associated flora and fauna.

Top priority consideration should be given to the plight of the mountain gorilla and its forest habitat, for in Uganda and Rwanda the tiny gorilla populations will survive only if more *positive* steps are taken to safeguard their habitat and enlarge it as soon as possible. There is no doubt that the future of the mountain gorilla will be in Zaire, and the final responsibility for its survival may rest with this nation alone. They will need active international help and encouragement in order to succeed. It is of paramount importance for the Zaire government to draw up an overall 'management plan' to ensure the future survival of the mountain gorilla. This will need a detailed survey of the status and distribution of gorillas in relation to the forest habitats throughout their whole range and careful mapping of the population 'pockets'. Some will be very small, and isolated by areas of unsuitable vegetation, agriculture or other barriers. Since it is obviously wishful thinking, and perhaps 'bad' overall management, to hope that the gorillas of all regions can be saved, then the greatest effort must be made to ensure the protection of as many large areas containing viable populations as possible. Fragmentation of their range into small, isolated pockets must be avoided at all costs.

The various areas will then need the formulation of their own management plans. The animals from areas which may one day have to be surrendered for other use could possibly be relocated into existing or newly designated park areas (the Ruwenzori mountains, for example, do not contain gorillas) or sold to reputable zoos having good records in the keeping and breeding of apes. Finally the designated park areas themselves will need their own management plans, to be integrated into the overall scheme. While these may require the controlled neglect of some areas of forest they may also need the artificial creation of some areas of mixed secondary/primary forest of varying ages, that is the 'ideal' gorilla habitat. The timber resulting from such operations would be most welcome to many of the local people who rely on it not only for building their houses but for fuel to cook their food. Therefore the provision of such an essential commodity could well temper any bitterness felt by the local people over their exclusion from newly designated park areas.

It must be stressed that the suitability of these rather drastic management practices (and other possibilities, such as the complete long-term rotation of forests and their fauna with agricultural practices) must first be tested by carefully controlled small-scale field tests before being put into large-scale use. What is needed is the creation of the correct forest mosaic which is ideal gorilla habitat, not the wholesale destruction of virgin forest, for in these areas live other rare animals and plants. The formulation of such management plans, and their subsequent application, will require accurate information from many disciplines, as well as the responsibility and determination to carry it through. The experiences of the Kahuzi-Biega National Park in organizing gorilla safaris have shown that, like other tourist attractions, these, too, can be a valuable source of income.

We cannot hope to attain perfection but, like nature, we must try to achieve the best possible compromise. Decisions about the management of land and resources must also be relevant to the needs of the people who actually live in or near the areas to be managed for wildlife. At all costs we must avoid the situation where land-use management, like so much of modern African culture, is what Emmanuel Asibey, Chief Game Warden of Ghana, calls 'a poor hybrid between traditional cultures and those of developed countries'. We must strive to make this hybrid full of vigour so that it will harmonize with

243

the many conflicts of interest it will encounter.

On my return to IRSAC from the Kahuzi forests for the last time I saw a most spectacular sunset. As the sun dipped behind the stark outline of the Mitumba mountains its last bright shafts sliced across the tree tops in the darkened forests below. Soon the gorillas would be building their night nests, the fireflies would start their nuptial dances and the night world of the forest would begin. In the villages fires would be glowing to prepare the evening meal. Patrice and his friends would be exchanging news of the day's adventures. The drums would beat, likembes would be caressed by skilful fingers and the forests would be praised in song.

Similar scenes would be occurring over much of central Africa; but changes are taking place rapidly – changes which threaten the survival of the carefully balanced forest systems and their rare animals. The governments and peoples of Rwanda, Uganda, and especially Zaire, are trying to ensure that the forests do survive, *often at great cost to their own national economies* – but the economic pressures on them are great. They need, and *deserve*, more international help to enable them to offset any short-term losses (from *not* cutting the forests down) against long-term ecological, aesthetic and ethical gains for the world as a whole. We *must* give them more aid in terms of expertise, training, resources, and hard cash to enable them to make their decisions about conservation and land-use management free from short-term economic constraints. They have already given a great deal and so the ultimate responsibility rests with the richer nations of the world, for we all have our part to play in ensuring that rare animals like gorillas will always have forests through which to wander.

Index

Index

vocalization [*contd.*]
8 121–3, 124; of Zaire gorillas
159–60, 187–8
Volcano National Park 22, 81
Volkswagen Foundation 135,
228

Wahutu people 84, 89, 91, 111
Watutsi people 44
weather, effect on gorilla studies:

in Rwanda 40, 44–5, 53,
72–3, 75, 90, 94–5; in Zaire
162–3, 167–8, 213, 239

Zaire 14, 15, 69, 97, 228; cattle
driven into 42–4; gorilla
population in 62, 87, 238–9,
244; National Parks of 132–
42, 241–2; agriculture in 137,
235–6